Dedicated to all the healthcare workers who have put their lives on the line every day to help us fight COVID-19.

COVER ILLUSTRATION: Avani Ahuja

All views expressed by interviewees are solely their own and do not necessarily reflect the views of the author.

CONTENTS

INTERVIEWS

PREFACE

AVANI AHUJA

We all celebrated frontline workers as heroes at the beginning of the pandemic for putting their lives on the line every day. We applauded their efforts in the streets of cities. We 3D-printed masks. Yet the pandemic continued. Our heroes were idolized but also expected to perform their duties day after day, even when mask guidelines were violated, vaccines were thrown in the trash, and healthcare workers were violently assaulted.

I wanted to find the stories of the people behind the portraits that we painted of our heroes. The narratives of healthcare workers were well-documented at the beginning of the pandemic, but a comprehensive documentation of the experiences of female and non-binary healthcare workers around the world did not exist when I started this project. I wanted to learn about the stories of single moms scared to transmit the virus to their children, pregnant women who felt like they weren't doing their part to save individuals during the pandemic, women whose coworkers had quit their jobs, and women who communicated with the families of patients. While interviewing or surveying these women and non-binary-identifying individuals online, I was struck by their perseverance to serve humanity, even when humanity wasn't serving them. In each interview, there was a resounding message of exhaustion and the sentiment that their sacrifices were simply being taken for granted.

The hope is that these interviews and online surveys will allow you to experience the pandemic from the lens of frontline workers who were putting their lives on the line every day. The interviews have been published in almost the same way they were recorded - the goal is for you to experience the voices of the interviewees in the most authentic form possible. The hope is also that these interviews will serve as a collection of primary sources for future studies of the pandemic - they act as a way of inserting a non-white, non-male narrative into the documentation of this pandemic, which has had a lasting impact on all of us.

I hope you feel the same overwhelming wave of emotions that I did when interviewing these individuals or receiving their responses.

I hope you feel inspired to take action by supporting the Dr. Lorna Breen Health Care Provider Protection companion bill in the House of Representatives, which is providing healthcare workers with mental health resources to prevent burnout. I hope you reach out to your healthcare workers and learn about their experiences. I hope you spread awareness about public health and encourage your unvaccinated neighbors, friends, and family members to be vaccinated.

And most of all, I hope you start talking - acknowledging, helping, and celebrating these individuals in the way that they deserve.

INTERVIEWS

"THE THOUGHT THAT WE'RE NOT GOING TO LET THIS WIN OVER US HAS KEPT US GOING"

DECEMBER 2021 (USA)

Q: How did you become interested in medicine?

A: My grandfather was a physician. As a child, I watched him work. During my high school, I would sometimes shadow him at his clinic in India. I think that was when I initially started getting interested in medicine. The subjects that I was interested in during my school years were science and STEM subjects. I think with my grandfather being such a positive influence on me and talking to him about some of the diseases he saw, sharpened my interest in it. Also growing up, we had a couple of family members who had health issues, that further spiked my interest in medicine as a profession and a way of life.

Q: How would you describe your overall experience, if possible, in a couple of words or phrases?

A: COVID 19 pandemic has been a learning experience for sure. It was scary to see how helpless we were because we did not have many tools to fight this virus. It was new to us in the medical community. We are so used to dealing with diseases and infections that we've already seen in our day-to-day life, the same pathogens. It was a learning experience. It was also a lot of transition. I would say, we've all grown so much in the last year, not just with regards to what we learned about the virus but also how we are dealing with it and the situation around us.

Q: *What has been the most challenging part of that learning experience?*

A: I am an infectious disease physician, so we are at the front line dealing with this. I think the hardest thing for me was dealing with ICU patients being sick for weeks and sometimes even months in the hospital on the ventilator and not having any family members close by who could hold their hand. It was us physicians and nurses who were trying to be their family members. All we could provide at least initially in the pandemic was supportive care. We had the supplemental oxygen, we had the tools to support them, but we didn't have any therapeutics that would cure them. That was hard.

Q: *Do you feel like the personal protective equipment and the masks were also inhibiting you from connecting on a more personal level with these patients?*

A: Absolutely! Not only with the patients but with other physicians and nurses on the team. We, in healthcare are used to working as a team - talking to each other, presenting articles, discussing patients, working as a team - but it is difficult when you have a mask on. One thing to remember is that most of our patients are elderly patients, and a lot of them have impaired hearing. They are tied down with all these tubes, and you have these strange-looking people coming in with these masks and gowns. It can be terrifying when you're in that situation. Communication is much harder, of course, because it's hard for them to hear us. The personal rapport that we used to have with our patients is harder to build now.

Q: *Do you feel like the mainstream media is covering the pandemic regarding frontline workers accurately? Is there something that they're missing out on?*

A: I think they have been pretty good. They have shown the plight of physicians, healthcare professionals, clinicians, nurses, and frontline workers well. Things are as desperate as they are shown in the media. We are all working hard, and it is getting to us. There have been some reports that are inaccurate in certain sections of media as is expected, but majority of reports are on point.

Q: *Segueing into my nonprofit's focus on female healthcare workers, how has your experience as a woman shaped or influenced how you handled the pandemic as a healthcare professional, and has it in any way been different from your male peers?*

A: It is difficult to compare. I think all of us have had a tough time, but I think being women, we align ourselves with our patients in a more emotional manner. At least, that's the way I feel compared to our male peers. At the same time, all of us have families. We are nervous about bringing the infection home to our children, parents, and our spouses. I feel that sometimes we can become very mechanical when we are taking care of so many patients. As a female, I tend to connect better with the families. When I talk to them on the phone, it's easier for them to speak to me and share what they're going through than it is sometimes with male physicians.

Q: *Is there any specific experience or specific story that you would like to share that you feel comfortable sharing?*

A: Well, I think there are so many. I mean, I have seen many patients with COVID, so it's hard to know, but one that kind of sticks in my mind. What grade are you in?

Q   *11th grade.*

A: It's a bit heart-wrenching. I took care of a 21-year-old female who was almost eight months pregnant, and she lost the baby. She got extremely sick and died a month later. It was determined later to be because of COVID 19. She was found to have a blood clot in the placenta, I think that stands out in my mind because this was a very young woman who was just about to have her first child and was looking forward to it. And two lives were lost because of this disease because we were so helpless against COVID. This was earlier on when we had just started seeing patients with COVID 19, and we didn't have any therapeutics. We didn't know as much about the virus. I still remember talking to her parents on the phone, and I think that's a moment I can never forget.

Q: What were her parents' reactions?

A: Parents who were excited about being grandparents for the first time...and then losing their grandchild as well as the daughter in one go...I don't think there is a word to explain what they were feeling at that point. I mean, it was a spectrum of emotions. I think they were just in shock. But there are so many stories like that. I mean, it's just unbelievable.

Q: When you're talking to these patients' families, how do you view your role in talking to them, and what kinds of things are you talking to them about?

A: While talking to the families you are trying to tell them what their options are and what you can offer the patient. There are steroids, and there is plasma, and there are some antiviral drugs that we can use. Initially, we discuss those options. If the patient is not doing well, we just tell them that this is what the situation is, the quality of life, and what the prognosis is. My goal and my role in this kind of situation is essential to give them a clear picture as to what's going on with their family members because this is an unusual situation and a novel disease. It is difficult for family members because they are unable to visit the patient because of isolation. We try to FaceTime and all that, but it's not the same. As a physician, I attempt to present a clearer picture and put things in perspective.

Q: What is it that has kept you going and has kept you motivated? And even for some of your peers, what has kept them motivated?

A: COVID-19 is very different from what we were used to. It's a new virus, but it's also very similar to the life and death situations that we deal with every day. There are other infections, other issues that we constantly are challenged with. It's just the nature of our profession. It has been a little more challenging because this has been a constant struggle for weeks and months there is no break in between. Every day is a tough day. The thought that we're not going to let this win over us has kept us going. We know that vaccines work in viral infections. We are constantly reading news and looking at research hoping for a breakthrough.

It belongs to a family of viruses that we've dealt with before, just a different kind. I knew there was going to be light at the end of the tunnel, for sure. We just didn't know when and where it was headed, and we had to get over this hump. I think that's what kept us all going. We know that scientists are working towards getting a vaccine for everyone. But by the end of the year, or the beginning of next year, it will be here for general population. And once it is here, it will get a lot better.

Q: *How has the situation been? I know you've touched on this a little bit, but especially with the development of a vaccine, how has the situation evolved from March until now?*

A: We do not see the impact of the vaccine really because we just started receiving it. I got my dose on the 18th of December, so it's...you know, it takes two weeks for at least the immunity to start building up. And even then, with the first shot, it's only about 50%. I will get the second shot 3 weeks after the second one. But I think the difference is that at the beginning of March, we were naive. We didn't know how long this was going on. We thought maybe we'd get a handle on it by June, especially when the lockdowns were going on. We were hopeful that the lockdowns would be able to cut back on the number of cases. I think by August, we were getting worried. We knew how bad things were. July and August were difficult in Illinois. March and April were bad for New York. But I think compared to that, once the vaccine was approved, there was a feeling of hope. We know that we will overcome this as long as all of us are consistent with getting the vaccine and getting immunized. We should hopefully be on the other side soon.

Q: Is there a story or experience you would like to share that my previous questions haven't covered?

A: I think it's because it's so positive. We had a gentleman about 60 years old male who was transferred to our hospital from a different facility where he was diagnosed with COVID; he was on the ventilator. He was very sick. They transferred him over to our hospital for further care. He was with us for almost 15- 20 days. He required tracheostomy, chest tubes and significant supportive care. And then about a week ago, he was awake, and he was sitting up in the chair, and he was trying to talk to his family on FaceTime. This was a patient who had been unresponsive for 40 days. Those kinds of experiences kind of keep us going and help us keep the faith. Things can turn around, and you must keep fighting.

Q: *How do you guide a patient who has been out for 40 days toward recovery, both mentally and physically?*

A: It's a tedious process because COVID has neurological consequences. This gentleman has been out for 40 days; he will require significant rehabilitation. He would need speech therapy, physical therapy. I mean, it's a long road ahead. Hopefully, he will continue to get stronger because, in the immediate period, he is frail and prone to strokes. As a step-down unit, he has been sent into a rehab kind of facility, and then after that, he would go home with home therapy and so on. It would be a long process.

Q: *Is there anything that you think could have been done better? Or do you think this was inevitable?*

A: I think we could have acted on it sooner, for sure. We'd started hearing about it in December/ January. The first two cases in Illinois were in our hospital. There was mixed messaging from the government...lockdowns in January and February could have helped a lot. I believe we can be more efficient with vaccination distribution, which is not happening yet. I mean, it was organized in the hospitals, but I think it's still not as well stocked in the pharmacies, I think there's a lot at the federal and the state government level that could have been done better.

Q: *Do you see anything positive that has come out of the pandemic and this experience?*

A: Many things. I think it has made us all more resilient for sure, and number two, I think it has made us humble. I mean, we are more cautious, more careful. I think if everybody develops the habit of wearing masks, that would be a real positive. We'll probably see fewer influenza respiratory tract infections. I think families have become closer. I think a lot of families are doing things together and trying to focus on each other. And I think that's a big positive.

In addition, there are fewer emissions and less traffic. People are a little more aware, so all those are good things. Even from a hospital standpoint, we have realized that we should have better stockpiles of things like PPE. The world is becoming smaller as people travel all the time. It's easy to see something that we haven't seen ever before. I think we learnt lot of valuable lessons, but there's been a hefty price to pay for it too.

Q: *How has your hospital suffered from a shortage of PPE or ICU beds?*

A: We were very, very lucky, and I think our hospitals, CMOs, and CEOs were very on top of things. We saw the first two cases in Illinois in our hospitals, and my partner, the head of infection control in the hospital, ensured that we were prepared with PPE before. We are in the Chicago suburbs, so we had time to learn from New York and Chicago downtown. We never had shortage or issues with PPE at all. With regards to the ICU beds, we converted a lot of our telemetry floors to ICU beds as soon as we realized that we were going to run short. We were pretty much total capacity, but we never ran short on beds.

Q: *You handle so many patients every day, and you've been talking about this feeling of helplessness. How do you move on?*

A: Patients do get better and go home, and that is encouraging. And that helps you to move on and allows you to come another day and try your best. I think that's been positive for us. And now, with the vaccine coming, we know that as more people will get vaccinated, the lower the chances of transmission, and the numbers are bound to go down. I think that's encouraging.

Q: *How has your family life been impacted as a frontline healthcare worker? How have they responded to your experiences? How have you shared your experiences? Have you shared them at all?*

A: I have a lot of friends who are physicians, and we talk with each other, and that is good. I mean, we don't share patient privacy issues, of course, but we talk about mutual concerns or patients that we are working together on. I think that helps to bounce off those ideas and thoughts. I share my thoughts and concerns sometimes with my daughter and my husband. Just when I'm a little overrun after long hours, need to talk to somebody. I share it with my children and my family because they need to be aware of what's going on out there. I think it makes them stronger. It makes them understand the importance, and I think that's the reason why they've been so good about quarantining themselves and staying at home and isolating themselves. They do understand what's at stake.

Q: *Is there a message you have for the people*

who will be viewing these experiences through the nonprofit about the pandemic?

A: This pandemic has shown us that we are all vulnerable, so we need to be kind and receptive to other people. We need to listen and help people in need. Stay in touch with your family and make sure everybody's doing well. If anybody's having issues, make sure you take them to the physician sooner rather than later. I would say more connection among people, families...kindness, just resilience, and vigilance. Listen to the public health messages that are coming. Be careful, and it's for everybody's good.

Q: *Do you feel like the pandemic has also brought you closer to your peers who are physicians and the people with whom you're working on the front lines?*

A: It has because we were going through the same experiences together. But at the same time, we are always constantly masked and gloved. It's hard to have that personal rapport that we used to have. Even though keeping your distance and all that is important, it has also caused this little bit of a gap among physicians because we are busier than ever. Nobody has the time to talk for too long. Everybody's just trying to do their best. Our days are longer, and everybody's just trying to do their work and go home. We communicate with each other, but that personal bond that you had by spending ten extra minutes is tough to have now.

Q: *In the future, into these next couple of months, especially with obstacles like snow and other weather events, how do you feel that's going to affect the pandemic? What sort of plans do you have for the future and what are the hospital's plans?*

A: I am hopeful. People will be meeting less due to cold weather. They will be eating out in restaurants less, especially in the snow; outdoor dining will be a problem. I feel that that might help cut down the spread of the virus. At the same time, with holidays, people are meeting. I recently saw that travel peaked with the maximum number of people traveling this past Sunday since the pandemic started. We may see a spike in the next couple of weeks related to that. It will be a brutal winter because even though people may not be meeting as much, the recent holidays and all will cause a spike for sure.

"IT WAS DIFFICULT TO EXPLAIN THE FEAR"

DECEMBER 2021 (INDIA)

Q: How did you become interested in medicine?

A: Actually, it was probably due to my parents because they also went to medical schools, and I was inspired by my father especially.

Q: What medical field did your father work in?

A: He was an orthopedic surgeon, a bone specialist.

Q: In a word, how would you describe your overall experience during COVID-19?

A: In a word, you can say it was frightening at first. But now I think we have come to terms with it; we have accepted it.

Q: What has been the most challenging part of the pandemic in these last nine or so months?

A: Hardest time was in the beginning when we did not know much about the disease. And so many patients were flowing into the hospital, and we didn't know what exactly the course of treatment would be. But now, because we have come to know certain things, it's just more streamlined.

Q: Has there been anything positive that's come out of the pandemic, or has there been anything that's been a little bit easier?

A: As in the hospital, I think the positive thing is the collaboration among different specialists. Like I am a general surgeon, so I was not into infectious diseases that much, but because of this pandemic, we were also supposed to give our services in treating COVID patients. We interacted with other specialties a lot due to this pandemic because the internal medicine people could not handle all of the patients, so we were also into it. That is what has never happened before.

Q: *Did you perform any surgeries on COVID patients? What exactly did your work consist of?*

A: Yeah, I had to look into those patients. We did not do any elective surgeries during the COVID pandemic. The emergencies, yeah, we had to do a few, like we had to put chest tubes in some patients. They were the things we were scared of previously, but then we got into those kits, the PPE kits, and then we got to do our work.

Q: *Do you feel like the media and the news have been covering frontline health workers' experiences accurately? Do you think there's something they're missing out on?*

A: Yeah, we can say they are, but they are missing the actual situation. Like, you cannot precisely explain the mental thing, the fear in the health workers which, now, is reduced. Previously, as the disease was new, we were terrified. Everybody had to do the work. It was almost like we were forced to do it. But now, as we have taken care of those patients, there is some familiarity. Like, surgeries have been conducted on COVID patients when needed, and the surgeon and the team have come out okay. They did not get infected. So the confidence of the COVID teams has increased. The people, even the staff, the doctors working in the COVID hospital, have been taken care of because of the PPE kits and all. It was not as if everybody who was going inside would get infected. So, previously, we were scared. I think it was difficult to explain the fear to anybody.

Q: Has India had any unique experiences as compared to other countries?

A: I cannot say about a unique experience. I can't say India has any because the population is too much here. I don't know the exact date, but the percentage of people infected in cities is very high. Our patients from villages and all have not been infected that much. In the cities, the people have had more infections. I don't know what the reason behind that is. Maybe the city air is more polluted; our lungs are already damaged. Perhaps we are more crowded in cities; that is the reason. But most of the village people have not contracted the disease, which I think is unique.

Q: How are the experiences different among various groups? Have the experiences of rural people, people living in the city, and people of different beliefs differed at all?

A: Yeah, that is what I was saying. They are neither wearing masks nor doing social distancing in villages, but then also they are less infected. The disease has not gone into the villages. But people in cities have more chances of infection. I don't know the reason behind that.

Q: Is it possible that some people in rural or lower-income communities are reluctant to come to the hospital because of the money involved?

A: The government hospitals are mostly free here, so I don't think that is the reason. Ignorance maybe, because primarily people have very mild symptoms like a fever and cough for a few days. So it might be that they do not bother about that and carry on with their day-to-day activities. They don't come to get themselves tested; that may be a point. But otherwise, we have not brought many severe patients from villages and rural areas.

Q: How has India, if at all, tried to reach these people and tried to spread awareness of COVID?

A: One was the lockdown; it was to reduce social gatherings. But because of the lockdown, people were forced to sit in their houses, so social distancing naturally was possible because of that. And because of the lockdown only, we came to understand that not going to parties, not going to malls, not going to crowded places can also be done, and that is also another new way of life, which we have to follow.

Q: *How has your experience as a woman, as a female surgeon, shaped or influenced how you have handled the pandemic, if at all?*

A: Actually, I don't consider gender bias a big part of my experience. But yeah, the family was a bit apprehensive. I was worried about my children also because I was going to the hospital and coming back to my home. And that is, I think, with other workers also...that was the main thing. Otherwise, previously, in the beginning, I was more apprehensive. But afterward, over time, we were also trained in how to do the things in COVID and out of COVID for non-COVID setups, but to take care of the special precautions, which have to be taken because of this pandemic. So routinely, the wearing of N-95s, hand sanitization, social distancing...now that has become a routine. Now I rarely go out of my house without wearing a mask.

It has become a part of life. So unconsciously, we

wear the mask. We do not touch; that is a point; we do not handle patients more frequently than previously. We wear gloves when we have to touch a person. Otherwise, we did not follow such, you can say, guidelines so strictly. That has changed.

Q: Do you feel represented as a female surgeon? Do you see a lot of other female surgeons where you work?

A: Female surgeons are few in India. But there are many female healthcare workers. There are so many nurses, staff, and other female doctors, so all are working. Nobody has skipped work because of the pandemic.

Q: Is there any specific experience you would be comfortable sharing or some story that stuck out to you?

A: My first experience was when I saw the first patient. I was in charge of the triage of my hospital in the beginning, most probably in March. We ultimately lost the first patient. We were not very familiar with the symptoms and the disease course at that time. The patient came to us; he was speaking. He was dyspneic but not that much, dyspneic enough that we could panic. Within half an hour, we lost the patient. We were shocked at how we were not able to save him. And after that, we, I think, learned a lesson that we had to act very fast when it's a suspected COVID case. So that was very painful, the first patient we lost. After that, we mobilized our whole hospital for things like oxygen to act fast as soon as the patient came to the hospital.

Q: *What is it that has kept you going and motivated after experiences like that? And what is it that has kept your peers motivated?*

A: The main thing which has motivated us is the teamwork of all the hospitals...I think the staff and administration because when you see others also doing their duties, you, I think, get inspired. That is what has kept everybody in motion.

Q: *Do you feel like masks and PPE have made it harder for you to communicate?*

A: Yeah, it has made working harder, but the PPE kit is used when we are in the COVID hospital, when we are just near the COVID patients. Masks we wear when we are in the OPDs, when we are in emergencies. So, wearing the mask is not that difficult, I think. But wearing a PPE when you have to wear it for so many hours is difficult. It is challenging to operate while wearing a PPE. Yes, it is very taxing.

Q: *What exactly does your PPE consist of?*

A: Our PPE is a full gown with a hood. There

are goggles, there is a shield, there are double gloves, there are shoe covers, everything we have.

Q: *As you look back on the past months, do you see anything that could have been done better?*

A: I think the hospitals and staff are doing a lot for the community. But the community is, I think, not doing that much because people are still not wearing masks. People are still going for gatherings. This should not be done. There is no way that they have not understood that COVID can be prevented by these simple methods: wearing a mask, social distancing, hand hygiene. We, as doctors, have understood. We, as hospital staff, have understood. But the people coming to us, they have not understood till now.

Q: *What would your message be to those people to try to incentivize them to wear masks and take the proper precautions?*

A: My message is just that you should not take things for granted. Life is very precious and doing just these simple things is not very difficult. It is not very difficult to do hand hygiene, wash your hands, and maintain social distance. It is not very difficult. They should keep in mind that, hopefully, it is just for a few more months. So, if they follow these rules, hopefully, the workload for the doctors will be much less.

Q: How has the situation changed between March or whenever the lockdown began in India and now?

A: Now, mostly the patients coming to our hospital are mild cases, and now home isolation has started. So, the workload has decreased. Only the severe patients are being admitted, which is also significantly less...the number is less. And all the health workers have been thoroughly trained in dealing with COVID patients, so the situation is more streamlined now.

Q: In the worst parts of the pandemic, when you were dealing with a lot of loss, how did you emotionally handle that, and how did you move on?

A: Usually, in the hospital, we were used to talking among ourselves. When we came home, we were used to talking to our families. They used to give us strength. That is what, I think, helped.

Q: Is there a unique story or experience that my previous questions have not addressed yet that you would like to share, or a specific aspect of your experience that you can share?

A: I'm a senior doctor, so I have not been there for an extended period. I've gone for surgeries. It was also a challenging time. Because of your specs and your goggles, there is fog, and it isn't effortless to see. It's tough to move in the operation theater while doing your duties. But the junior doctors primarily used to have so many long hours of tasks wearing the PPE kit, which was very difficult for them. My juniors used to tell me, "Ma'am, we are sweating profusely." ... used to be almost 100mL to 200mL of sweat in their shoe covers when they used to come out. It was so difficult for them. They have worked very hard, I think.

Q: Do you see your female peers getting affected in a different way than your male peers, or has the experience been equally hard across genders?

A: I don't think there is any difference between both genders. It was difficult sometimes for those people where both husband and wife are in the COVID ward. Although, it was ensured that both would not go for COVID duty simultaneously. So definitely, it was for the younger ones who had small children; it was difficult for them to leave their children behind for three weeks or so, not meet their family for so many days and live-in isolation. That is, they were actively isolated when they used to go for their COVID duties. And then they used to go to hotels to stay. It was a difficult period for them. Yeah, it wasn't easy to remain away from your near and dear ones at such a time.

Q: *How did they deal with that isolation?*

**A: **They usually used to talk or have video calls with their families. And that was, I think, what kept them going. And also, when you see that all others are doing the work just like you, you feel you have to do it, and then you are determined to do it properly. I think that is what kept them going. They used to talk to us; they used to share their experiences with us. It was frightening at first, but then over time, it was like, yeah, everybody's going for three weeks, then coming out. And they used to be tested after coming out. Then on the fifth day also, they used to be tested. But mostly, they all were negative, all the health workers...so the fear went away. And I think that was a better time.

Q: *Do you feel like masks and PPE have also made it harder for you to communicate with patients on a more emotional level?*

**A: **Yeah. It is challenging, and you do not touch the patient as much as you usually do. Like, I am a surgeon - touching a patient before doing anything was a way to start some communication. It showed compassion. But now, we do not do that anymore because of COVID.

Q: *Is there anything you've been doing to replace*

that in some ways to try to still make an emotional connection with the patient?

A: We try to talk more.

Q: When you have a patient who has a very severe case, what is your goal in talking to them? What are you trying to communicate?

A: We first try to make sure the patient does not panic. We try to comfort the patient verbally. It is difficult, especially when the patient has young children; it is tough to tell them that he's serious and may not make it. Also, it's essential to talk to the relatives outside, which is also very difficult sometimes.

Q: When you share these experiences with your kids or your family members, do you communicate all of them, or are there certain things that you leave out? How do you present these stories and share them, and does that help?

A: I usually tell them that they know that the disease is severe, and they also take things very seriously and have to follow social distancing. Like, children sometimes pressure parents to go outside, go to the gym, go to the mall, go to school. Although the schools are closed over here, there was an option that we could send a student to school if the parents allowed it. So, mostly nobody's sending, but maybe a few people are going to the school. It was difficult for parents, mainly to keep the children home. Like my children, I think, feel that we are the strictest parents. Other people are not following those norms, but they had to. We used to tell them, "This happened in hospital today, this person came who was very sick. Sometimes the entire family is infected, the father, mother, children." So that was what we used to share with the children and tell them to tell others to please remain in their homes and don't go outside; the lockdown is for the good of society.

Q: *When you run into people who aren't following restrictions, is there anything that you say to them?*

A: It is difficult to say something to people you don't know, so I think I never say that. We tell the people in the hospital to wear the mask properly. Sometimes they don't know. They have not covered their nose, or when they speak, they pull the mask down and start communicating. So, we tell them, "This is not the proper way; there's no use if you are doing it like that."

Q: *So, that's about all of my questions. Did you have anything else you wanted to ask me or share?*

A: I just wanted to know if you have other female workers who told you something different, like the experience is different for the other gender?

Q: You're my second interview, but I've heard something similar. I think what I've heard about being a female healthcare worker is, one, that connection with your children where you don't want to leave them behind. And the second thing is sometimes female healthcare workers feel like they can connect with the patient's family on a more emotional level than their male peers can, or the families feel more comfortable talking to a female healthcare worker than a male healthcare worker.

"SOMETIMES, YOU FEEL LIKE SOCIETY FORGOT ABOUT YOU"

JANUARY 2021 (USA)

Q: What got you interested in medicine?

A: I've always wanted to be a doctor. I think it was initially the fact that my mom wanted me to be a doctor because she wanted to be a doctor. But her circumstances didn't allow her to go to high school. I was also always interested in the field of medicine. It's just something I love doing. I like medicine so much because this is a field that is also a service. I'm always connected with my job, and the human aspect gives me great job satisfaction. If you talk to doctors, most doctors will say they don't want to retire. I think being a number cruncher would be very boring for me. I just love medicine because of the diversity, human connection to it, and its service aspect.

Q: In one word or phrase, how would you describe your overall experience during the pandemic?

A: I don't think you can describe it in one word. It was horrifying to see so much misery. In the beginning, we didn't even know exactly what we were dealing with. We found out later that this virus also causes blood clots, and a lot of complications arise as a result. We thought it was just a respiratory disease, but people started getting heart attacks, strokes, and blood clots. This virus causes clots everywhere - in tiny blood vessels, small blood vessels, and big blood vessels.

Q: *How has this situation evolved between March 2020 and now in terms of your preparation levels, your emotions in handling the virus and what you know about the virus?*

A: We really know a lot more now. Now there's therapeutics, and we have treatments. People are coming in, and they're getting sick, but we can turn them around without them going to the ICU or requiring a ventilator because we have good treatments now. We have dexamethasone, and we have an antiviral called Remdesivir. Now, when they come in, they get worse, and then you give them these treatments, and then they get better. The first time around, some people were spending 60-70 days in hospitals, and some of them never got better, and their lungs got destroyed. Or they became brain dead because of the stroke, or their heart stopped, and then they had complications from that.

But this time around, we have seen a lesser severity of the disease, or if the disease is severe, it gets treated quicker than before. And now there is a vaccine. The first time around, we were also fearful for ourselves and our families. People had made a considerable amount of sacrifices - people were not staying with their families, and mothers were separated from their children. My daughter lived in Wisconsin with her dad, and I was supposed to see her for spring break. I had taken time off, and once I canceled that; we were separated for four months.

There were many, many stories like that. I didn't get it, but many of us got COVID. Some of us died, and some of us got seriously ill. We had a lot of fear. But now, most of us are vaccinated, so there is the hope that there is an end in sight at some point. Although with the second wave, we're just feeling tired. And then you hear, and you see people not wearing masks and people calling it a hoax. People say they're COVID fatigued; they just don't understand what the healthcare providers are going through. What about us? And now we're getting back to where we were in the spring. It's very frustrating for a lot of us. We have to deal with it. But it's different from last time.

Q: *What is it that has kept you going? What is it that has kept your peers going? How do you move on emotionally from each experience when you have to deal with this concept of loss on a regular basis?*

A: I advise young people that if you want to make money, then go into the field of business or finance. Because I do feel that to be in the world of healthcare, it takes special people. And the collegiality that we saw at first, where everyone - old, young, surgeons, non-hospital doctors, primary care providers - just chipped in and said this is what we have to do. And they did it without any complaints. We had no PPE, and people helped each other. For example, some young doctor in California who was a friend of a friend was making face shields via a 3D printer. He sent me 100 face shields.

Among healthcare workers, there was so much generosity, and there was so much collegiality. That's really what kept us going. You felt frustrated and disappointed by society, but then we saw each other. For people who are in healthcare, we are used to putting ourselves last. We show up to work sick. Now they're saying, "If you're sick, you don't have to work." That's just something that's in our core. We are strong people, we're resilient people, and our bond with each other just grew stronger during this pandemic.

That's what's kept us going, along with our commitment to the world and our patients. When we take the Hippocratic Oath, it says, "Do no harm," and we take it seriously. We just are, again, putting ourselves last. We did get a breather in the summer. It's so reminiscent of spring. Even though, logically and at a conscious level, I know that it's not going to be as bad. I got my second dose of the vaccine on Tuesday, so I know that I'm going to be okay. And my patients - most of them are probably going to be okay too. But everybody's feeling the emotional memory that we have and they're tired. We just don't know how long this is going to go on. And we feel disappointed in society since all you have to do is wear a mask.

Q: How has your experience as a woman in your profession or in the workplace shaped or influenced, if at all, the way that you handle the pandemic in the workplace?

A: I'm a feminist. I am a multi-tasker, I have a daughter, I have a family, and I am a nurturer. So, in my field of medicine, I bring that nurturing quality to my profession. That's what shapes me. And it has helped me cope with it. Women can cope with a lot more. We start menstruating at age 12 and we deal with our body changes all our lives. We are used to coping with adversity more than our male counterparts.

Q: In these past few months, is there any specific experience that you feel comfortable sharing?

A: There was a patient who got COVID in the summer, and she was a nurse. We were taking care of her for 60-70 days in the hospital, and then we couldn't get her off the high flow oxygen because of low oxygen. She was so nice, and she was always thankful. I just felt so helpless. There was also another patient who was with me and then others in the ward where we were dealing with more stable patients. Because they got worse, we sent them back.

I'm always an optimistic, happy doctor, and I give hope to my patients. I always say, "The positive thing about this is this." But then I had to explain to him that he had another lung collapse, he needed another procedure, and we needed to put a chest tube in. He spoke another language, but he said to me in English, "I am disappointed." Because that's my usual mantra to say to patients, I said to him that the positive side of this is...and then I couldn't think of anything positive. I ended up saying, "The positive side is that you're at a great hospital." This is the best I could come up with. So yeah, that feeling of inadequacy and helplessness was personally very hard, and it still is, but I'm more comfortable with it now. It was also hard not to be able to touch my patients. I like to hold their hand, I like to sit with them and talk, and I could do none of that. I felt like a robot, and that bothered me a lot.

Q: *Do you feel like the mainstream media is*

*covering the pandemic regarding both frontline
workers and female frontline workers accurately?
Are there things you think they might be missing out
on, or they could be doing better?*

A: I don't think that they're making any special
coverage for female frontline workers. I'm not
saying it's harder on women. Still, I'm saying that
the media is not covering more stories of healthcare
workers' ordeals. But I think part of that is also that
many healthcare workers who work for hospitals
and organizations cannot just go ahead and give
interviews to everyone. So, that could also play a
part in it. But yeah, in the media that I listen to, I
think they do cover what frontline workers are
facing, but then other things take precedence like
political events that are happening. Sometimes, you
feel like society forgot about you.

Q: *Do you feel represented in your field as a
female doctor or in the workplace that you work in?*

A: Yes. Things are better for women, but we still
have a long way to go. It has been well-established
that for the past 20 years, there are more women
in medical school. But if you look at the top
admin people, the deans, the division chiefs and
department chairs, they are white men. And for
diversity, yeah, you can say they're about diversity,

and you can create diversity departments. But that's not what we want. We want representation. There need to be women. There should not be a glass ceiling, but there is. You see more women in leadership positions now. There is more representation than there was, but there is still not enough.

Q: What has been the hardest part of these past months, and what do you think could have been done to make it better?

A: The most challenging part of this past year has been coming to terms with the fact that this didn't need to happen. We have the best healthcare system. We have the best public health system. The fact that we're a failure is what hurts. A lot could have been done better.

When President Obama left in 2016, the White House had a special initiative. There was a playbook on the pandemic, and that was just dismantled. There's a TED Talk by Bill Gates. There's a speech by President Obama from circa 2014 about pandemic preparation. So why were we still not prepared? Lots of things could have been done better, and we were capable of doing them. The healthcare institutions feel like they're on their own, and that's very disconcerting. Testing also should have been done better so that we wouldn't have even reached the point where we are.

In March, when we were admitting patients, we were giving everybody hydroxychloroquine. That's what they did in Italy and in China, and we thought initially that works, but it doesn't. We were all just doing everything only in clinical trials, and that's why the positive things that have happened are a result of an extreme collaboration among scientists, among countries, sharing data, sharing viruses and genomic, wireless morphologies. Sharing data with each other is why we were able to create so many vaccines in such a short time. So, the thing that could have been done better would have employed the really good public health systems that already existed.

Q: *Building on what you had said about a collaboration among scientists, do you see anything positive that has come out of the pandemic?*

A: Yes, lots of collaboration. We had so many people volunteer, and so many people just said, "We're surgeons." People came in and worked as interns under medical doctors so that they could help out. We were running out of beds, and people from out of state came and helped. The benevolence and magnanimity of healthcare workers has just been tremendous. The collegiality among women has been incredible. But in this field, in healthcare, it really has been men and women, old and young - everybody. So, I've never felt proud of my colleagues like I do now, every one of them. I mean, they are amazing people. Amazing. I don't know what we would have done without each other.

Q: I don't know what the country would have done without you. Building on an earlier question, what are some of the differences between the experiences of female frontline workers and non-female frontline workers? Are there any fundamental differences, or are those differences a result of discrimination?

A: No. I think there are fundamental differences and cultural differences in American culture too. Like for your generation, my daughter's generation, and even the younger generation of women in their 30s, it's probably going to be different. But in the past, women always moved or sacrificed for their partners. As women are becoming more successful, their husbands don't offer as much, or it doesn't work that way. Also, when my daughter was young, one of my colleagues used to say, "I'm so tired working all day. I go home. I tell my wife that I just want to be on my own for 30 minutes before I'll see the kids." And I told him that I can't get away from work fast enough so I can see my daughter. I don't want to wait another 30 minutes.

I think that's the basic fundamental difference between men and women. I mean, you can say that you can't generalize it, but I think you can generalize that we're mothers, so we take the extra responsibilities of raising our children. And as I'm talking to you, I'm stopping at the grocery store and buying things so I can go home and make tomato soup with my daughter. She texted me and said she wants us to make tomato soup today. You won't see a male surgeon doing that with them, but some of them do. It's changing. The world is changing. We're trying to change it so that the next generation of women coming forward will not have to deal with what we had to deal with.

Q: *Is there anything policy-wise or any improvements that can be made in the workplace that will help this situation?*

A: Yeah. I think that having a longer maternity leave would help. For example, in Canada, you can take up to a year of maternity leave. And here, it's six weeks only. If you want to do more than that, then you have to go without pay. Also, people are always weary of hiring young female doctors because then they feel like they're going to have a baby. So, we definitely need to be working towards more gender equity by improving things like maternity leave.

"I COULDN'T CONTRIBUTE TO WHAT MY COLLEAGUES WERE GOING THROUGH"

MARCH 2021 (USA)

Q: How would you describe your overall experience over the past year or so in a word, if it's possible, or even a phrase?

A: It's been challenging in ways that I could never have imagined. So maybe challenging would be the one word, but that would be the phrase. That's all I have to say.

Q: What has been the most challenging part of this past year? On the flip side, what has anchored you?

A: I think it's been the unknowns of how the pandemic was going to unfold, and every step of the way, not knowing. I had a unique experience as a physician, a female physician who's also a mother. I had a new...how old was she when we actually...? Hold on, she was about a year old. Yeah. I had a one-year-old, and I was pregnant with my second child. And there were a lot of unknowns of how this virus would affect pregnant women. We know that viruses, in general, affect pregnant women more because they're in a relatively immune-suppressed state. So how it would affect me is something that I had to think about. My husband is also an ICU doctor, and so we are a physician family.

My husband is in pulmonary critical care. He was actually in the throes of it. He's in a hospital and basically was seeing COVID patients day in and day out. And we didn't know how safe we needed to be. At that point, everything was still just in question and unfolding. And so that was a really big challenge for our family as we had this one-year-old. I was pregnant with my son, and my husband was isolating from us because he was seeing COVID patients, as I mentioned, without adequate PPE. He was given an N95 to wear because there was a shortage. He was given it to wear over extended periods to reuse it. It was very nerve-wrecking.

He stayed. I have this image of him in my mind where he came up to get dinner, and I handed him dinner over the baby gate that we had over the stairs to him, and he just took it back downstairs to eat by himself. So that was the kind of isolation that we had in our family. And as a female physician who's pregnant, it was a lot to process and many unknowns. We had a rule in our hospital where you couldn't go into the COVID unit if you were immunosuppressed or pregnant. So, that affected me emotionally in different ways. It made me feel like I wasn't contributing when my colleagues were stressed, and then I delivered. I took maternity leave because I was postpartum, and I had these two. I had a newborn and a one-year-old at home.

It made me feel like I wasn't contributing. It was a whole other emotional element that I didn't realize would exist. I think female physicians specifically have some other aspects of dealing with the pandemic that I think aren't necessarily known or addressed. And so, when I heard that you were doing something like this, I felt that it would be valuable to share some of those thoughts and feelings.

What I felt, I think the worst was not helping my colleagues. So because I was not basically in my hospital at that time, as a pregnant woman, I was not allowed to go into the COVID unit. I couldn't contribute to what my colleagues were going through. That's what I think I felt the worst about, yeah.

Q: What could have been done to make the situation in the past year go a little bit better for healthcare workers overall, and even possibly for your unique situation?

A: I think two big things come to mind. One, that people would have actually listened and would wear masks and stay home and had followed the guidance set forth by the CDC because that would mean less exposure and therefore less exposure to us on a personal level, and so that is one. Another thing would be, I think, having some sort of...it's been said many times that doctors are burning out, that there is just overall low morale, if anything. Doctors had to take pay cuts during this time in many hospitals. Thankfully, I did not have to, but that is just something that physicians have been going through in this pandemic. And I think some government-led effort to thank doctors and say, I don't know, if it would be...whether there was a push for loan forgiveness or there was a push for just some kind of compensation, I think, for people. Yeah.

Q: *Is there a specific experience that you heard about that you would like to share or some story that stood out to you?*

A: Well, I can share two. One is not my personal experience with the patient; it's with my husband. He had a 34-year-old patient die whose mother had died the day before, both with COVID. So, that to me was...I think that's a lot to deal with emotionally as a physician, to take care of dying families. And then I think for me, just for the families not to be able to be there physically for their family members... and that's being echoed, I think, everywhere. But it is something that I think is scarring and affecting the emotional state of healthcare workers, to see people die alone and without their family members.

So, the one story I have to share is...I was talking to a wife about her husband, and he had asked me to relay the message to her because he was going to be intubated soon, which means to be put on a mechanical ventilator. And he said, "Tell my wife I love her." I told her that, and she started crying over the phone, and he died after. So the last thing that she heard was through me. And I felt like I was really glad that I took the time to ask the patient, "What do you want me to tell your wife?" And so just to have that disconnect where she wasn't at his bedside...he couldn't tell her directly. And that we, as healthcare providers, communicate those sorts of things...it's very emotional.

Q: How have you and other healthcare workers handled this concept of loss, or have there been any sort of provisions to help with that, especially because there's been so much of it during the pandemic?

A: You're saying basically loss of life, loss of patients?

Q: Yes. How have you and other healthcare workers coped with that?

A: I'm not sure that...I think the recognition that doctors are burning out, that nurses are burning out, healthcare workers in general during this time is essential because once you recognize something, then you can allot resources to help. And so far, there hasn't been a more significant push to help. I can tell you that, basically, any of my friends that are dealing with this and have seen so much loss... nobody has reached out and said, from a hospital administration standpoint, "What can we do to help you? What's important?" It's been internal colleagues discussing it, but I think that it's been rough, you're on your own to cope, you're on your own to figure out what your best mechanism is to release. You are stressed, but there isn't any support that people are being given. It's just you on your own. So, for me, if you're asking me, it's just been communicating, just talking to family and things like that.

Q: How has having to wear a mask all the time and having to socially distance all the time impacted the way that people have collaborated and communicated in a hospital setting?

A: I think wearing a surgical mask is something that anyone can do all day. There's no excuse for that. Sure, when you're breathing, it can dry out your eyes a little bit. There's the air that comes up, but you've got to push it down, etc. There are certain discomforts with it, but it is not new for us as physicians to wear a mask for prolonged periods.

But the N95 mask is quite uncomfortable, and add a face shield on top of that... And then you have difficulty hearing people because they sound muffled. It's been challenging in exciting ways in that...in a code situation, in a case where the patient isn't doing well, you need to hear each other well. Communication has been a barrier to that extent. And many people have had a breakdown of their skin, things like that from wearing N95 masks that have to be tight fitting.

Q: Specifically reverting to female and non-binary healthcare workers, issues like musculoskeletal diseases have been shown to affect female healthcare workers disproportionately. Have you or any of your peers had personal experience with these issues?

A: Your question is...female physicians with musculoskeletal issues not related to COVID, you're saying, just in general?

Q: Just in general.

A: I have seen more rheumatoid arthritis in some female colleagues. That's my experience with it, but I can't think of others.

Q: Do you see anything positive that has come out of the pandemic?

A: I think it has brought people to work together.

I believe human beings are incredible in that they can come together and do incredible things when working together as a cohesive group. And I think working with scientists, clinicians, and the medical community just blew me away during this pandemic. It's just been such an overall positive and empowering response. And I also think that people there had been kind of focusing on business aspect of medicine, and people forgot who doctors are and what we put on the line to help others.

And for the first time, I would say in my entire career, from medical school onwards...it is the first time that I truly felt that people were thankful, as a whole, as a society. And it didn't feel like it was all about business, which is what is happening to healthcare, unfortunately. And it felt a little bit like doctors could be doctors and get the recognition they deserve in a pandemic.

And I don't mean just doctors. I mean healthcare workers, so throughout. But that's, I think, a positive that came from it. People realize what we do.

Q: *What is it that keeps you going and motivated? What is it that keeps your peers going and motivated, especially throughout such a hard time?*

A: Just helping others. That's what I know to be true of everybody. Everyone just wants to make sure that as many people as possible come out on the other end of this pandemic well. And so, I know that's what drives them and drives me.

Q: *Do you feel like the media has been covering the pandemic with regards to healthcare workers and specifically female healthcare workers accurately? Or do you think there's something they're missing out on?*

A: I think they've been portraying healthcare workers very heroically, and I have no issues with how they've been portrayed. I would say, to be specific, with The New York Times, The Washington Post... But I worry that the way that Dr. Fauci was treated on certain news networks, specifically Fox News, things like that, where a doctor who was speaking for the benefit of people, who has devoted his life to helping others was demonized in that way. And to whatever agenda they thought he had, that was a little disheartening to see, to see that science wasn't sort of valued, and that a physician could be treated that way just for trying to help others. So that was disheartening.

What's interesting is that, as always, I think with female physicians, I can say specifically there was some social media posts, and some kind of opinion pieces, about what happened with women in research...that a lot of women were given more administrative tasks to figure out what the logistics of COVID patients in the hospital would be. And that male physicians were given more scientific studies, like doing research, and were able to publish. Still, I think that would be an exciting look retrospectively once the pandemic is over, looking at how many females first and last authors there are of publications. I think there was a big discrepancy, and some alarm bells were going off at the beginning of the pandemic. I'm not sure that it got better, but I know personally that it was voiced by many of my female colleagues.

There was 50% enrollment in medical schools of females and males in 2007. That was the first year that it was 50-50. And it's been pretty much 50-50 since that point, which is great. But there's still a little bit of a delay in terms of the attending physicians. I don't want to say at that time it was still 30% of the workforce was female. I would say it was about eight years ago now when I looked into this. So, it probably is closer to like 35%. Yeah.

Q: *Is there any other unique story you experienced that my previous questions have not* *addressed, or any topic relating to female and non-binary healthcare workers that you would like to share?*

A: Specifically, with COVID or just in general?

Q: *In general, or in relation to COVID. Either one is fine.*

A: In my women in medicine talk, I am very interested in many aspects of women in medicine. But I don't know if you have a specific question that I might help with. If you leave it very broad, I think I could probably talk about this topic for three days straight.

Q: *If you could classify the big issues that female healthcare workers face broadly, how would you categorize those issues?*

A: Promotion, and there are many aspects to that problem, including publications - the academic currency. And that ties into COVID a little bit but is our intellectual currency. And the timing of finishing training and trying to get publications out is the exact timing for most women to have children and start families. And so that is something that has come up time and again...the lack of promotion of women. Even when you correct for women who don't have children, women don't get promoted. Still, there is a significant slowdown of the careers after having children, of the women who do have children.

And even with males helping at home, which is like a societal change that we see in survey studies, they still show that women have more responsibility at home. When children are sick, more often, women will take off work than men. More female physicians are married to a full-time spouse, as opposed to male physicians who are often with a part-time spouse who can essentially take care of the home life more. So, I think promotion is a significant issue...publications, that's one of many.

"THEY DIDN'T FEEL HEARD"

MARCH 2021 (USA)

Q: *How did you become interested in medicine?*

A: Well, I wanted to be a veterinarian. I was interested in science and just, like, taking care of animals or people that are sick. Unfortunately, I realized a lot of veterinary medicine would involve having my own business, not doing what I wanted to do if people couldn't afford to do what they wanted to do for their pets. And so that was going to be hard for me. And it just felt like there was more scope for learning and doing more scientific stuff as a human doctor than a veterinary doctor. So, that's sort of how I decided to do medicine.

Q: *In one word or phrase, how would you describe your overall experience during the pandemic?*

A: I mean, it's been really...it's been interesting, right? So I went up to a state with a high rate of infection for some time early in the pandemic to volunteer. So, it's definitely...I think it's more complicated than I thought it was going to be. And I'm grateful that I was able to help. In a word, I'm not sure. I mean, interesting, I guess, is the one word I would use.

Q: *What has been the most challenging part of the pandemic?*

A: The isolation. Not just for us, but I'm an

intensivist. I work in ICUs, and our patients never talk to us anyway. Well, not never, that's not fair, but a lot of them have breathing tubes or they're on devices or they're sedated, so they don't talk with us, but we're used to interacting with their families at the bedside, and we're able to explain things at the bedside and sort of communicate. And so, this was very different, and having patients that families weren't going to be able to see...they didn't understand. "I brought someone I love in who was coughing, and you're telling me that they're dying and have no other medical issues? I don't understand." So, the isolation is what families felt more than us. And it was isolating for us. Usually, when we go through something stressful, we all sit together, we get coffee together, we might even get dinner afterward together. But all of these decompressing situations, I mean, these moments of debriefing that we would typically have for ourselves for our sanity...we couldn't have in the middle of the pandemic. So, very isolating for everyone in it.

Q: Within the hospital setting, do you feel like you haven't been able to communicate as effectively with your colleagues?

A: No. I think I have been able to communicate generally okay because people have had a lot of acknowledgment of the fact of what we're going through. And it's great to see everyone sort of step up and help and go out of their way to make sure that we're okay. It's been nice to be able to communicate.

Q: *How has your experience as a woman in the workplace shaped or influenced how you handled the pandemic, if at all?*

A: I don't know how, as a woman, it would have been remarkably different. I think women physicians are a vast generalization, and I don't want you to believe that this is true for everyone, but in general, it's hard not to provide compassionate care. And I think that's true for my male colleagues as well, but in particular, I believe women found it a little bit more challenging.

Q: *Is there a specific experience that you've had in the pandemic that you would like to share that stood out for you?*

A: I think caring for people, having to care for someone that is a colleague of yours is very difficult. We're used to taking care of patients. It's hard when your colleague becomes your patient. And that someone...I didn't know that person because I don't work in New York, I was just volunteering, but everybody else I worked with had worked with this person for years, decades. They knew this person well. I think it's always hard to care for someone that you've typically known. It was hard to care for younger patients. We were prepared to care for patients with comorbidities, people in their sixties or even fifties. It was tough to care for patients in their twenties, thirties, and forties, young parents with young kids. That was hard.

Q: *How have you or your peers coped with the incredible loss of life that has occurred during the pandemic?*

A: I think it's been helpful to talk to people who have gone through a very similar experience, and I don't believe that therapy is not beneficial in any way. Of course, that is helpful, but I think talking to peers who have gone through very similar experiences or feeling the same way you do is helpful too. And a sense of...I've never worked harder than I've worked right now. And yet, I feel like I've never provided worse care than I have right now. That's a very frustrating feeling.

I feel like I don't have enough resources or just not enough people, and to feel like you didn't do the best but you did your best but that was not good enough in any way... We've been provided a lot of resources, and so that's been great. But I think more so than anything else, it's easier to talk to someone who's gone through a similar experience. So having friends and colleagues that I could share my knowledge with or hear their experience, which is very similar, was more helpful.

Q: *Did you ever have to ration care?*

A: Yep.

Q: *How did you make those decisions, and how did you handle them emotionally?*

A: I didn't, and that was very helpful. It was made by the administration or by physicians who were in that position to make those decisions. Rationing care in the sense that we ran out of ventilators might have happened at the beginning of the pandemic. I wasn't a part of that. I did not experience that. What I experienced was we had to share continuous dialysis machines, or we would run out of certain medications, we didn't have a particular antibiotic, so we'd have to use something else, or we'd have to make do with what we had. That kind of rationing of care. And then if you have like 26 patients, 20 very sick patients, and you only have two beds, you take the most unwell of those and the ones you think are going to do the best. I didn't make those decisions, but I agreed with those decisions that were made.

Q: What do you think could have been done to make the pandemic better?

A: I think earlier understanding and essentially earlier shutdown. I believe the ignorance that people had was fascinating. I don't understand how people walked around. Everyone has had primary science education; I don't know how people thought this would not be an issue.

I don't understand that. I mean, this is a pandemic. We've dealt with Ebola. It's a respiratory virus. We've had SARS-CoV-1. I mean, the idea that people were just like, "Oh, it'll just go away..." I was like, "With what magic do you make these kinds of assumptions?" That I didn't understand, honestly. I don't know why it took us to the point where we're out of beds. We can't care for you. We have to say things like, "We might not have enough ventilators for people" before people are like, "Oh, okay. This is a problem."

I don't think anyone in the healthcare industry...I don't know how many people you've spoken with, but none of us felt like, "Oh, surprise! This was going to happen." No, we were expecting this to happen. We've been waiting for the next pandemic to happen for years. We've been preparing for this. We are always tight on beds, and we never have enough ICU beds; we never have enough resources. We've known this. When we already raised alarms and red flags, saying, "This is not going well," and it took weeks before you're like, "Oh really?" When all of these patients suddenly show up in the hospital, you can't care for them. For people to realize that this would be an issue...I don't think anyone in the healthcare industry was surprised.

Q: *Do you feel like the mainstream media is covering the pandemic regarding healthcare workers accurately? Is there something you think they're missing out on or something they could cover more?*

A: I think it's kind of...it's almost surprising, where healthcare workers, nurses, in particular, physicians, respiratory therapists are being painted as like these heroes that are doing amazing things. It's just strange because this has been our job for years. I don't think any of us feel like heroes in particular, or at least I don't. I can't speak for everyone else. I don't feel like we did anything different or weird or super compared to before. We do this every day. We risk our health every day to try to help someone else. And we try to do it as safely as possible, but the idea that people had to do this without PPE, without resources...I think those things are a little bit strange. So that...I feel like we haven't addressed that. And we haven't addressed the fact that there are people in my profession who want to leave work due to the pandemic. I can't tell you the number of nurse practitioners, physician assistants...and they don't want to leave because we had to work hard or didn't get to go home. It's because they, at some point during the pandemic, felt unsafe because we didn't have enough PPE or because they felt like people were covering all of the bad things that were happening, and no one's minimizing the economic issues or any of the other issues. Still, they just felt like we've been saying this for years. They didn't feel heard, I think. It is not an insignificant number of people that don't want to come back to this profession. Some nurses are leaving ICUs. We always have a critical shortage of ICU nurses. I think it is something to think about. Based on what has happened in this pandemic, I don't know how many more people would want to go into medicine or especially the kind of medicine I do, ICU medicine. I worry about that. I worry about the future.

Q: *How do you think we could counter that sentiment?*

A: I think by providing adequate resources for the patients, right? And then, long-term, providing sufficient mental health resources, aids for nurses, preventing burnout, helping physicians to avoid burnout.

Q: *By burnout, are you referring to mental or physical burnout, or something else?*

A: Both. Unfortunately, both. Because it's at specific points of the pandemic when I think I worked 15 days straight, 15-hour shifts...15 to 16-hour shifts. And that's not...for me, that was not on the higher end. I know that there are people in smaller towns, smaller hospitals where there's just one intensivist who has worked almost two months straight.

I don't have kids. I have a dog, but I have to coordinate daycare. Certain daycares are only open at certain times. Just trying to do basic things during those times has been very difficult. Raising a dog has been compared to raising a kid very frequently. You can argue about that either way but trying to raise a kid or do all of this yourself with minimal resources is very hard. I feel that way, and in some ways, it's even harder, right? Because you can get daycare resources for kids, but sometimes you can't for dogs. And I mean, where am I going to leave my dog for hours at a time, right? And if you have an easy dog that everyone gets along with, great. If you have a dog like mine, where you're looking for resources or things, it's very hard. I wish I could say that it was easy, but it's been tough just to find items. So yeah, no, it's not easy.

Q: *Going off a previous question, do you feel like the mainstream media is giving enough attention to female and non-binary frontline workers, especially nurses?*

A: I don't think so. I think the frontline media, the story, or at least the way I see the story...and again, this is my perspective...everybody is a hero. They're working hard. This is so awesome. That's great. That's one narrative. But I worry about the other narrative. What are these people saying? They're saying they don't have PPE. At one point, we were accused of selling PPE or hoarding PPE for ourselves, when we weren't even doing that. We barely had enough for ourselves, let alone to hoard or to sell. And I think a lot of people were very upset about statements that were made. And then, I don't believe that there's enough coverage... that we don't address why there's this shortage here, why, primarily even before the pandemic, nobody wants to do this job. And if we have people that don't want to do this job, and now we've put them in this challenging situation, they don't want to do it. I think we're asking for trouble.

Q: *Do you feel represented in your field?*

A: There are very few women intensivists. And I feel that there's adequate representation for me, but yeah, it can never hurt to have more women intensivists because I believe the hours we keep, and our profession's expectations are very different. I think it's very hard for a lot of my friends to balance family life.

I mean, you're asking profound, outstanding questions. You're making me pause and think about my life decisions. Yeah, no, I think it's a hard job to do as a woman. There's a reason women choose not to do ICU medicine.

Q: *Is there anything that could be done to help more women and non-binary individuals enter your field?*

A: I think if we had better hours and significantly better childcare and better family resources. I mean, more daycares...most people I know have to get, like, a full-time nanny, additional resources. It's very few places that are supportive of physicians that are working these hours. And if you were a single mom, forget about it. It's nearly impossible. So yeah, if we had more family support resources. We have limited maternity leave, minimal everything else, besides this. So yes, I think we would need much more support for women to do this sustainably.

Q: And, I guess, have you seen any presence of musculoskeletal diseases in your peers?

A: Everybody in my field has plantar fasciitis, some kind of back pain, some kind of hip pain resulting from constantly standing. All nurses have plantar fasciitis. If you want to know what shoes to wear, just look and see what the nurses are wearing. They're always, like, going in and out of the rooms. Yeah, I would just stare at a nurse's shoes. You'll see it. We all wear the ugliest shoes you have ever seen because what we're trying to do is keep ourselves comfortable for as long as possible. So yeah, everybody in this field...everybody has foot pain and back pain. That's just what we have.

Q: I feel like nobody knows about it. I had to dig through and research this topic very thoroughly to figure out these issues.

A: Oh yeah. And then there's a night shift thing, right? We switch between days and nights. When I switch between days and nights, I can only sleep like four to five hours during the day. When I have to do three or four nights in a row, I am exhausted when I get to my third or fourth night because I haven't slept for a while. And then the nurses...if you have kids at home, it's not like you can sleep for eight hours during the day. Nope. You wake up when your kids are up. You take care of them. You have to do everything else and have a full day on the side while you're also working nights. Night shift, in particular is challenging.

Q: *Have you also seen mental health issues rise since the pandemic began?*

A: Absolutely. I've seen PTSD, but not just that - like, anxiety, depression, lots of burnout. I've told you, there are plenty of providers...it concerns me that I know plenty of providers that are not coming back to medicine or who have already left.

Q: *Has there been any effort to support these people?*

A: There has been. I think most institutions recognize that we're losing nurses; we're losing people that we've trained. So, they've made mental health resources available, but I don't think that's enough. Most of these people are leaving because they feel like the administration does not support them.

There are more significant issues that require more than just "Let's talk about this." And so , we fix those core issues...and anybody who tells you that we'll be done with this pandemic, and we'll be done is crazy, right? The next pandemic is around the corner. Hopefully ten years from now, but unfortunately, I'm still going to have to live through the next couple of pandemics in my career. Right? People don't want to do this again. We don't want to go through this again. Unless we can promise, as a system, "Hey, we're going to hire enough people, we're going to make sure." For example, if you're doing a dangerous job, a lot of people get hazard pay. That's because you put your life at risk.

We in the medical field never get hazard pay. Beyond that, forget the hazard pay; when the pandemic happens, most hospitals make their money through their outpatient procedures, like surgeries that they offer and things like that. Because we had to stop doing those things, a lot of hospitals took away our benefits. I took a 10% pay cut.

And I worked at lovely places. I worked a 10% cut. And all my colleagues in New York took a 20% pay cut. In addition to working harder, they took a pay cut. You work more hours, but you also take a pay cut. And if you don't, if you refuse to do it, you're made to feel like you're the worst person ever. "We're not going to provide you with daycare resources when all the daycares are shut. We will offer you nothing, but we'll take away your money and expect you to work harder."

I know you're recording this, and you're going to put this up there, but these are well-known institutions that took away the entire retirement fund, and yet the CEOs are making like 10 million. I'm just putting it out there. People are risking their lives, literally.

That would be great. I'm not asking to be paid. I'm not asking for special treatment. I'm not asking for any of these things. I'm just asking for the basics. For the most part, like in New York, many restaurants started to donate food. We almost always had lunch. It was hard. We had no place to eat, but I felt terrible that restaurants had to do that. It's okay that they did, but one would have hoped that administrations would have done a little bit more.

Q: *Would some sort of compensation after the pandemic or a long-term infrastructure plan help with a future pandemic?*

A: I think that would be helpful. Some places have given pay raises to people they thought worked particularly hard in the pandemic, so mostly intensivists and hospital medicine docs. So that's nice. But I mean, I think it's small things like that.

I think it's just acknowledging what we're doing. I believe painting people as heroes, like, "Oh, you're doing such a great job," is more dangerous than doing real things like supporting them personally. I mean, it's nice. Those things are lovely, don't get me wrong. And I'm not saying don't do that. But I think when you sort of symbolize someone and put them up on a pedestal as doing such a great job, it almost makes it harder for people to complain or ask for things. Rather than doing that, providing real resources might have been a more productive thing to do.

Q: *What is it that has been keeping you going and motivated? For your peers who have remained in medicine, what has kept them motivated?*

A: The hard part is, despite how miserable I sound, right, I love my job. I do. I think it's the most incredible job. I like doing what I do. It wakes me up in the morning. It gets me excited to go to work. The day it doesn't do that, I would quit because it's not worth it. So far, I do love my job. I like taking care of patients. I enjoy helping people. Just having that one person do well is worth all the 20 people you fought for that haven't done well.

We keep going because of that. And then having supportive friends and family. Even though

I'm isolated from them, I feel like, in some sense, I've seen some of them even more because we've done more zoom meetings, given more of an effort, and, like, having the support of my friends and family. When I went to New York, people would call me and check on me almost every day to ensure I was okay. That has been very helpful. So even though I might not have felt supported by the executives that I was working for, and again, I'm not saying that it wasn't right...some of them were very supportive. Still, even though I might not have felt as supported by some of these institutions, I never felt not supported by my friends, family, and peers. So that was helpful.

Q: Is there a unique story or experience that my previous questions haven't addressed that you would like to share?

A: Let me think. I mean, there are so many. Like, if you asked me for sad stories, I could give you 20. That's the unfortunate part. There are a couple, I mean, there are unfortunate, hopeless ones, but I can't decide what's a good one to share with you, to be honest. I have some good ones, some not-so-good ones.

Oh, you know what I will say? Aside from COVID, I'm also a hematologist and oncologist. I take care of cancer patients. A lot of cancer care and other primary care just didn't happen while we were in the middle of this pandemic. People had died waiting for their transplants because we could not do transplants. They waited while we were trying to do their next chemo round. We gave them what we would not normally do. I think the collateral damage from all of this is something that we're not even talking about.

Q: *Do you see anything positive that has come out of the pandemic?*

A: I think it's shown the resilience of human beings of what we're willing to do. And I've seen how, even when you don't have enough resources like nurses, people go above and beyond to make sure that patients are cared for. I've seen...I've had to do things...like, when I see people die and I know that I would never want someone I love to die like this, I try to go above and beyond to make sure that we're there for them as they're dying so they're not dying alone. No, I think I've seen a lot of resilience and the human spirit. It makes me realize why I do this job. I've seen people way older than me with comorbidities who have died due to doing this job. One of the chairs...he died while taking care of this. I've learned a lot.

We usually leave family members with

someone they love as they're dying because we want to give them space. Since they weren't available, I've seen people just sit there for hours. I've taken care of dead bodies because it didn't make sense for nurses... like, they were so limited, trying to take care of the live ones. So, I learned how to just feed and care. I've learned a lot of humility, and I've seen everyone go through this. They don't feel alone. That's why I don't feel like we did anything. These are the people who do this every day.

The nurses have been doing this for years. Like, what kind of person becomes a nurse except the type who wants to help people? I think, for the most part, it's been very humbling. I don't feel isolated. I don't feel alone. I don't feel supported by hospital administrations and government officials. And I worry long-term about what's going to happen. But in terms of peers and colleagues, it's been an excellent experience.

Q: *What message do you have for the public?*

A: To just, like, hear us when we tell you that we're going to run out of beds. Having people still not want to wear a mask or, like, saying nonsense is so crazy to me. I don't understand. We're going through all this. All I'm asking is for you to wear a mask and not get admitted to the hospital, and you can't even do that. I don't get it, honestly. I just don't know what to say. I don't. I don't get it.

It's just really frustrating. People are like, "You can't tell me what to do." And I was like, "Fine. You can come tell this family member that their 22-year-old is dying." You're willing to come in here and tell me that, or you promise me that you're not going to come into the hospital, like people going on spring break in the middle of a pandemic. Families are gone. And I don't understand how people don't understand or why they don't believe it. I mean, what would we possibly want? Where people are saying that we're making money out of your deaths or nonsense like that...it was one thing to be painted a hero, which I didn't think was necessary or agreed with, but it was another to be painted a villain, which is, well, way extreme. I don't get that. I don't get, like, not wearing masks. We're asking you to do one essential thing, and you won't even do that. And you'll protest against it and make it into a freedom thing. I don't get it.

It doesn't matter what your political beliefs are. Everybody gets sick. Unfortunately, no matter what your political views are, you will get sick. And when you get sick, you want us to care for you. And we can't care for everyone if you all show up in the hospital simultaneously. That's just a logistical fact. If everybody shows up at the same time, we cannot care for you. It's just logical; we can't care for 30 patients at one time. And to not understand that basic idea is crazy to me.

Q: *I'm assuming you saw different attitudes in different states.*

A: Masking is optional, more optional in some states. I saw what a proper shutdown looked like in my state. I didn't see a car on the street in the morning.

Parks were deserted. It looked like a ghost town. I didn't know when people were walking their dogs or if they were even letting kids outside because I didn't see anybody out; it was very different than in some states, where it felt like masking was optional and people were still dining outside well into when those states were peaking in July. They had a late peak when there was a lot of death. The death toll in the Navajo nation was ridiculously high. I saw there was just a lack of acknowledgment.

We don't...none of us wants to go through this again. And the next time this happens, we're going to lose a lot of people. Nobody is going to come back. It's not going to go well. And we all know that COVID, with the variants...we're looking at a potential surge. And if that were to happen, I just feel like we don't have enough nurses now, let alone what will happen after another surge occurs.

"THE PANDEMIC BROUGHT OUT THE WORST AND BEST IN PEOPLE"

MAY 2021 (USA)

Q: What made you interested in medicine?

A: It started with my aunt dying of breast cancer in 2004 back home in Togo, West Africa. She lived in France for almost 20 years, but she became sick back home and died. I can just see my mother and my grandmother depressed, but they didn't know what to do about it. So that's one of the reasons why. And then when I came here, I started with psychology, but then I looked at nursing, and I would see nurses, and I was like, "Okay, I like this job." So, I got into it.

Q: In one word or phrase, how would you describe your overall experience during the pandemic?

A: I would say it was horrible.

Q: What was the hardest part about the pandemic?

A: There were a lot of hardest parts. First, it was the lack of supplies, PPE, the lack of masks, and the lack of hand sanitizer. Gloves were not the issue, but the lack of rooms with negative pressures because the pandemic, as it started, was like the airborne type. So, we needed some negative pressure rooms. There were none of those. Also, at some point, some hospitals had to use the same N95 for a day, a week, and so on. So, that's one of the horrible parts. Then I started as a new nurse in February. I began on

February 24th, and then starting March to mid-March, the pandemic started. It was hard for my preceptor, and it was hard for me as a new nurse, to begin with, to learn and be overly anxious first about the job and then about the pandemic, because in retrospect, we work, we went to school so we can do the nursing and then the pending income and then we don't know if we will ever make it or not. So that was the horrible part of it.

Q: *What do you mean by negative pressure rooms?*

A: There are some diseases that are airborne. TB is one of them that can transmit easily. Yes. So, at first, the idea would be to get a negative pressure room to be isolated. They do it with negative pressure because the air that circulates in the room doesn't come outside the unit.

Q: *Could you clarify what negative pressure itself means?*

A: They have COVID in the airways, like in the air, because the patient who's the host may be in the room coughing and doing everything. But because the room is set up so that it only contains negative pressures, the air won't be flowing back in the unit and contaminate those that are not COVID positive.

Q: *Oh, so there weren't any more of those rooms?*

A: Yes, because each unit, it's usually like I'll say six of those. And two on each side of the unit. There was...I think there were 10 in our unit, and that's it. The third floor was considered a COVID unit, but the overflow of patients was coming up. Then maybe we had like 15 persons that are either COVID positive or a patient under investigation. We learn that there's a COVID test that's pending results.

Q: Is there any specific experience from this pandemic that stood out to you that you would be comfortable sharing?

A: Well, I'll say that the pandemic brought out the worst and the best in people, and because COVID visitors were not coming in, a lot of patients were dying alone, even the ones that were not COVID-related like a hospice patient. This patient was maybe 91 years old. In normal instances, family members may come to pay their respects and say goodbyes.

Because of COVID, which was just like chaos, and no one knew what was going on, family members were not allowed to come into the unit. So, there was one incident where a patient was...I'll say 38. And she had metastatic breast cancer that went to the brain. This patient had three children at home, and I'll say they were nine, 12, and 13 years old.

She was dying, and she became a hospice case patient. The only people allowed to come were two of her children, I think the ones above 12 years old. Because below 12, you cannot come into the unit. That's just a regulation. But then I had to go and talk to my charge nurse, and I said, "This patient is only 38, and those children are going through such trauma that it would be cruel of us not to allow these kids to come and see their mother." So, the charge nurse called, and then they allowed all three children to come into the unit. And that was just a moment that I remember till today. It was just sad.

That view was just something that I don't...I don't wish on anybody. That was one of them. And there was a lot of it too, moments when nurses will come and help each other or they will not come and help each other because people are overwhelmed, overworked, and overstressed.

Q: *How has your experience as a woman in the workplace or a non-binary individual in the workplace shaped or influenced the way that you have handled the pandemic?*

A: I think it taught me that I have to speak up because as you know, in the medical field, the doctors, mainly the men, the main sex you will see is male. And that when some of them tend to be chauvinist like they don't really...I don't think they have respect for women or even respect for the nursing job. With that regard, sometimes maybe a resident, because every July 1st, they come and start the practice.

But some of them may come in entitled and think, "Oh yeah, I know this, and I know this," and they don't... Most of them go and don't even say hi. They just walk into the patient's room and stuff like that. But there's just basically the nurses. They help you. It can either help you or make your life harder. So, I just learned how to speak up for myself and know when not to overwhelm myself with trying to help someone when I know that they need to learn.

Q: *Did that issue get worse, or did it get better during a pandemic where people were so overwhelmed in the first place?*

A: It got worse. The reason why is because there's so many times, I recall the doctors would not even go and see the patient, but you may see in the notes they did see the patient. I don't know. Maybe I wasn't there. I'll assume I wasn't there.

But in some instances, you may be at the bedside all the time, and the doctor may come and say, "Oh yeah, is this patient doing, okay? I will ask you several questions," and then he'll go and do a report as if he spoke to the patient. He did this, or he did that because everyone was scared of actually coming in contact with a patient that had COVID in the beginning because it was new. The death rate and the virus were just so novel to all of us.

Q: Is it true that the nurses were often the ones who were putting themselves at risk?

A: Yes. Most of the time, because when the call light comes on, if the patient presses the red button, it comes directly to the nurse. Nurses are overwhelmed, and we are left to do almost, I'll say, everything. This, that, this, that, people call you even for the lab. Pharmacy calls you to ask you about the medication that the patient has on record. I don't know how, but maybe because of our gender and because we feel for people, we care. I think a lot of responsibility they push onto us. And I don't think we should accept that. That was, yes, that was the one, a nurse that was a nurse for almost 40 years. I asked her and I said, "How did we get to this point?" She said, "I don't know." She just said that she wonders what that's about, or yeah. A lot of things that, instead of saying, "Oh, no, I'm not doing this," nurses will just say, "Whatever, I will just do it," and that's not okay.

Q: I've also seen statistics that say that issues

like mental health or physical disabilities have been shown to disproportionately affect female and non-binary healthcare workers, possibly because of the issues you just named. Do you have any peers who have had personal experiences with these issues, or have you observed these issues in other places around you?

A: Honestly, I think I observed it during COVID almost. I would say...I say 85% of the entire staff was stressed. Stressed, anxious, and some you can tell they were depressed. Not knowing where it was going to go... Having the choice while they are around me, sometimes people say, "I don't want to wear the mask because it's my right." Do you know? But in the meantime, like when a holiday comes...I remember this nurse, she said that "we are just left like sacrificial individuals, because I don't understand how you can call someone a hero, but you turn around and you don't want to follow the rules and regulations because when you come back, we cannot just say, "Oh no, we don't want to take care of you." After all, that's not ethical for any of us, so why?" And she makes a good point. This is going to be PTSD that we have to deal with our entire lives, I think...

Q: *Did your workplace do anything to help you*

or your peers with those mental health issues? Did working conditions get worse? Did the hours get longer? Were wages cut? Did they try to help in any way?

A: Well, they try to help money-wise because they increased the incentive. We had a contract with those that are courageous enough to go ahead and sign an agreement that they will. So, they tripled the salary, well, the hourly rate, they tripled it. For them to have the courage to go ahead and take care of patients that are COVID positive I think helped a lot because people had a clear understanding of who wants to go and work with COVID patients and who isn't forced to do so.

Some people would say, "Oh no, absolutely not. I'm not signing any contracts." Some went ahead and signed the contract. Yes. So that was a good thing. But then the downside was that many people, because of COVID, were just quitting, quitting, quitting. The workload was becoming a lot for those that stayed. And I think it's still the case today because nurses quit their jobs, and they're like, "We're not doing this."

Q: Do you think having some sort of organized mental health service or economic compensation help with the with the anxiety and depression or monetary losses that healthcare workers have suffered?

A: No. Well, personally, in what I've seen and assessed, I don't think so. Compensation... yes. Because I don't believe money alone could alleviate the trauma that people went through. Even though it helped partially, it was eventually just the commotion, the chaos that the pandemic brought. And I would tell a hospital, and they tried to get us, like, free mental assistance, mental health assistance, stuff like that.

Q: *Did it help anybody you know, or did it help you?*

A: It didn't help me. What helped me is to talk to my friends. For example, I spoke to them about what I'm going through. That's what helped. Talking to someone that I don't see can relate...when I see you can't relate to the struggle, I can't find any healing. That's just me. Maybe I'm biased. Yes. I think talking to my peers that can relate tremendously helped.

Q: *Do you feel like the mainstream media accurately covered the struggles of female and non-binary healthcare workers during the pandemic? Or is there something you think that they missed out on?*

A: I think they missed out on it. I think overall...

they didn't even mention gender bias or how gender does play in the binary, that does play a lot inside this. Because on the other side, they say that a lot of women lost their jobs because of the pandemic because of school not being back in session and kids were forced to stay at home. People couldn't work, so women lost more wages than men out there or even on the spectrum. I think yes, they miss out on it because even nurses, they lost their jobs. If they were single ladies, like single mothers, they were not able to find a babysitter.

Q: *Those things were not covered in the news?*

A: No, no. It was not covered. I didn't see any coverage of any of those. The plan was to just pressure care workers, like, "Oh yeah, they are the hero," but I really didn't understand the hero part because everyone has a role to play in this. So, that was my concern. I was like okay, all of us have a part to play in this. It's just not a hero thing. No, you make your claim, and I do my part so we can move in the right direction.

Q: *So what you're saying is that healthcare workers cannot just keep saving people, but people themselves need to be responsible.*

A: Some compliance has to be in place. But well, I guess we live and learn.

Q: *What do you think could have been done to make some of the hardest parts of the pandemic a little bit better?*

A: Well, we were unprepared for this, supply-wise, and this shows a discrepancy in the socioeconomic status...ratio...and just emphasized it to the point that you can see that the poor were getting sicker and dying a little more than one that would be well off. And even when it comes to the supplies and stuff like that, we shouldn't be having issues with supplies when we are putting our life on the line to begin with. So that alone...I think we need to work on that. And now I think I would start buying the supplies and saving them because we just don't know. I don't think that's the best idea, but that's what I'm going to start. In case we face something like this again...just not blindsided.

Q: *When you or your peers experienced loss, especially as you were surrounded by death during the pandemic - how did you deal with that? How did you move on emotionally if you're comfortable talking about that?*

A: I will say 80 people died before I came into nursing. So, that wasn't...I'm sorry to say this, and it was hard because the age was not restricted to older people. In hospice, it may be the elderly, or it may be because we were taking care of people between 18 and 110.

Well, I've seen people who are 18 years old die, and that was home care. But when it came to the pandemic, all of us were unprepared. We just saw code blue after code blue, and even coworkers, coworkers' family members, coworkers' children, parents were dying, so it was hard. But working that, I will say praying...prayers kind of helped a little... and positive affirmation. That's it.

Q: *What was it throughout the pandemic that kept you motivated, and what was it that kept your peers motivated?*

A: I would say family. Yeah. Family. The last ones that people have, like the people you love in your life, will be the ones that will give you the drive. Yeah. I think that's it because either way, it was not because of our nursing self. It was not because...it was just because of the people that you love. And the patients...are you going to abandon them at this point when you know there are no nurses that are coming, and if you don't show up, maybe the care will be less, you know? So, it was all that.

Q: *What message do you have for the public?*

A: General public? Let's say be compliant. And live your best life. And each one's best life may be different from the other but live your best life. And mainly live today like it is the last, because all of us... because tomorrow is not guaranteed. So, I think that will be...yeah. Either way, one person that doesn't want to get the vaccine just lives their best life. Well, your freedom stops where the other person's freedom starts. So, be respectful, be respectful of others' decisions and what they want to do too. Yes, with that in mind, live your best life.

Q: *I know you've touched on this a little bit, but do you feel represented in your field?*

A: In nursing and, I guess, in general, in medicine...in retrospect, compared to the generation before us, I'll say yes. I think we are in good shape, and I'll say that we are on an excellent path to progress. Yes. Compared to the other generation like maybe 30 years ago, 50 years ago.

Q: *Do you think there's room for progress? If there is room for progress, what do you think would help us move toward that?*

A: I come from a background where, back in the day, I would say 30 years ago, they didn't value women going to school. That's back home.

But my overall opinion when it comes to everything...when it comes to females, women, is that we have to teach our girls that marriage and having kids is just not enough anymore. We have to be educated because I think the world was built for men when it comes down to it. We have to speak up now, and we have to advocate for ourselves. We have to be educated and understand that we have many things and a lot of progress...we have a lot of things to do. Yes. Education is the number one. And to others, we have to emphasize the need for education. I think that's where I stand.

Q: Do you see anything positive that has come out of the pandemic?

A: I do. It taught us that we are stronger than we think we are. We think we have control of maybe all the parameters surrounding our life, but no, technically, we don't. And that's like a dilemma because on the other side, we can make a positive impact on our lives too. We can choose to be prepared. We can choose to be prepared to be cautious and to be careful as we go. But I think it showed many people that first, the healthcare system was not that great and needs more effort put in it. And if it's the case in America, let's not even talk about developing countries. Because it seems like they are behind by, let's say, decades. There's still a lot to do when it comes to that. It showed us that we just have to think a little bit more than we were doing.

Q: *Finally, is there a unique story or experience that my previous questions haven't addressed yet that you would like to share? Or is there something else that you would like to discuss?*

A: No. I think I also value...I'll say one thing. I also value the power of having good leaders. I think that does play a role. Just put it that way.

"WE HAVE A PRESENCE THAT CAN MEAN SOMETHING TO A PATIENT WHEN NO ONE ELSE IS ABLE TO BE THERE FOR THEM"

JUNE 2021 (USA)

Q: How did you become interested in medicine?

A: Well, I have a former degree actually in journalism, so I love writing and storytelling, but along the way, I met a lot of healthcare providers. I have a few in my family. I have an aunt who's a nurse. And just growing up, I spent a little bit of time in Central America where I worked on different healthcare teams, like non-clinically. I got to observe what they were able to do and felt like the impact was huge with their skills. And so, I'd say, like, that was in the back of my mind. And then, I don't know, I just decided to start looking into nursing, and then I had a chat with my aunt, and yeah. I just found myself pursuing that after a lot of thought. And it's been an awesome decision.

Q: In a word, or if that's not possible, a phrase, how would you describe your overall experience during the pandemic?

A: Honestly, I would say the word would probably be exhausting.

Q: What has been the hardest part of the past year, or what has been the most exhausting part?

A: Well, I'm a new nurse. The most exhausting part has been having first to learn how to be a nurse and get good with my clinical skills while also being surrounded by the context of a pandemic and just the stress involved in that. And I can even see in some of my classmates I graduated with who have pretty intense jobs in the ICU that the burnout is already there. We've only been nurses for a year. I don't know if that answers your question.

Q: It does, thank you. Are your pronouns she/her?

A: They are, yes.

Q: How has your experience as a woman in the workplace shaped or influenced how you have handled the pandemic, if at all?

A: Hmm, that's a good question. I primarily work with females who go by the pronouns she/her, so it's hard to compare. Still, I would say what I feel to be true would be the concern that being a woman during the pandemic, as a healthcare worker...we have, I think, an added concern for our families, especially if we have children. I go to work, but I want to be really safe because I know I'm coming home, and I have a family I also have to take care of. I don't want to get sick or bring that into the home...I think a lot of my coworkers would share that feeling. I have two, and my oldest is almost three, and then I have a four-month-old. I definitely have that in the back of my mind. I'm working on something that you don't fully understand, and you don't know for sure. Especially at the beginning, how exactly to be safe or if, like, the measures you're taking to be safe are effective. And there's always, like, that added stress and exhaustion of, like, am I doing the right thing for my family right now?

Q: *What do you think could have been done to make this pandemic a little less exhausting or a little less challenging and burdensome on nurses in particular?*

A: Oh, I think...so when I initially started as a nurse, I was at a hospital that was in the community, and I felt like there was a lot of lack of communication, especially among management to nurses. There was a lot of confusion about the protocols that were in place and the steps that were to be taken to keep people safe. And so, I feel like communication definitely could have improved. I hope that if there's ever another pandemic, hopefully there isn't one in our lifetime, just that there would be faster communication and less confusion...clear directions to nurses to help mitigate that exhaustion.

Q: *Is there a specific experience from the past year or so that really stood out to you that you feel comfortable sharing?*

A: I work in a pediatric unit and I'm with children who are...they're quite sick. And at the beginning of the pandemic, we were only taking the sickest patients, which is always hard to see, but something that really did impact me was the fact that because of COVID, the number of caretakers who would usually be allowed to come visit or be there with the patient was minimized to just one person. And so, of course this child often has, at least usually, two parents, usually siblings, usually aunts and uncles who are concerned. And for me, that was probably the most impactful, just seeing that family dynamic being impacted when a member of the family was sick.

Q: *These are children who are not necessarily really sick with COVID, right?*

A: Correct. Yeah. I did not work in COVID units. They're usually children with just separate disease processes, like, for example, leukemia or anemia. Yeah.

Q: *Following up on what you were saying, how did COVID affect the way that you were treating these patients? I know you were obviously at limited capacity.*

A: We had to...with every patient that comes into my workplace, we treat them as if they are potentially positive. It does minimize, so we didn't have as much freedom to go in and out of the room. We always had to be wearing full PPE, which is necessary to keep everyone safe, but also, it's a barrier. These kids are unsure and it's sometimes their first time in a research center or even a hospital. I feel like that definitely impacted the dynamic of care that I was able to offer. And then, yeah. Just...I feel like that was probably the biggest thing.

Q: *I've seen some studies where issues like mental health or physical disabilities have disproportionately affected female and non-binary healthcare workers. I've also read that this is especially true in physicially taxing professions, such as intensivists. If you're comfortable sharing, have you or any of your peers had personal experiences with these issues?*

A: On a personal level, because I was pregnant during...when the pandemic started, and then I had a baby in the middle of it. And I can definitely see where I struggled, probably additionally, because of the pandemic with just feelings of isolation and anxiety, but I can see it in my peers. I have a good friend. She's nice, an ICU nurse in a COVID unit. And she absolutely struggled with anxiety and just dreaded going to work, even though she's only been a nurse for a year. So yes, absolutely. I see that as true.

Q: *Do you feel that the way media is covering the experiences of female frontline workers is accurate, or is there something important that you think they're missing out on?*

A: Huh. That's such a good question. I feel like there was a lot more coverage of healthcare workers in the beginning. I could be wrong, but when it first started, I feel like that was sort of a highlight, but I do wonder if in the years to come, we'll have more mental health issues in healthcare workers than what the media is really able to accurately report right now, just because we don't have all of that data yet. It might be definitely more of an issue of just time will tell.

Q: *Oh, I see - so it might take some time for the trauma and burnout to set in.*

A: Exactly. Yeah. I do wonder about that. Like the trauma that, like, hasn't really surfaced quite yet.

Q: *Do you feel represented in your field? That means either as a nurse or just in medicine in general.*

A: Represented in what way?

Q: *By gender specifically.*

A: Yeah. Well, I think nursing is a highly female dominated profession still even with worm hill coming into it. Yes, I do. I would say probably, for the most part, the nurse leadership where I work...the majority are women. So yeah, I do.

Q: *What is it that keeps you going and what has been keeping your peers motivated?*

A: Definitely having conversations with each other that are really honest because you need... there's a lot of people, like, who aren't going to understand what our experience is. It's very personal and specific because a lot of people were able to work from home during the pandemic, but we were essential workers, so we had to go to work. I think that's been a huge thing, just finding people to talk to, but being motivated by the fact that we have skills, and we have a presence that can mean something to a patient when no one else is able to be there for them. And for me personally, that is a huge motivator that I have access to when, for the most part, the whole country, and the world has been shut down in a lot of ways this year.

Q: *Although this is unrelated to COVID-19, in the pediatric center, how have you moved on emotionally when you have experienced any sort of loss at work? Do you talk to your peers about the losses that you experience? For your peers working with COVID patients, how do they move on emotionally from each loss?*

A: Since I've been there, we have had a few patients die, and I would say, because I'm new, it's still something that I am learning how to handle and I'm still developing those skills to cope with it. But I think again, it's just knowing the resources of who's safe to talk to, to process that. And then for my friends who are in COVID units. This year has been really, really hard as far as death goes. And I think for them, it's knowing to recognize the moments when the emotions are at a point where you do need to seek out outside care, like whether that's a therapist or a group session that's facilitated by someone who's a professional to really be able to debrief and effectively process that because it's a lot.

Q: *Do you think some sort of mental health support initiatives directly funded by your workplace would help with some of the issues that you are your peers are facing?*

A: Yeah, absolutely. I feel like my workplace is good with that, but I don't think every hospital is, so I would say yeah, 100%.

Q: *What message do you have for the public? This can be based on what your experiences have been or what you've observed around you. This answer can also be specific to your location or* *the behaviors you have observed in specific people around you, like family members.*

A: Well, I think something that I found to be interesting is kind of what I mentioned earlier, how the media sort of has shifted away from highlighting...started off as healthcare workers are these heroes, but then I think it's kind of like something...I don't know... You don't have to put this in an interview, but I kind of compare it to being a new mom. The shifting goes from, like, the mom and pregnancy to the baby, and the mom gets kind of forgotten. And I feel like healthcare workers... there is a tendency to just kind of think, and I've seen this in, like, older, more seasoned nurses to sort of just expect...like, well, this is their job. This is what they're supposed to do. And sort of, like, take out the humanity of what they're experiencing and the trauma that they're experiencing, day in and day out, especially those who have been working from the very start of the pandemic. And just not normalizing it, I think, is something that I would want to share with the public because it's...yeah. It's a hard job that they're doing, and it shouldn't be taken for granted. That's what I would want them to know.

Q: *Do you see anything positive that has come out of the pandemic?*

A: Yeah, I think that I've seen...let me just think about that. Because I have. I think I've seen people. This is more like family wise, but I've watched where my own family and other families...I know they reconnected because they have had to sort of be forced to FaceTime or text. And I think that's been a huge thing. And also, on the healthcare front, I think that this pandemic exposed a lot of places where there are weaknesses, and I hope that that's going to cause improved healthcare infrastructures. And I hope that a lot of disparities that were revealed through the pandemic get addressed. I think in those ways it has had positive aspects. Obviously, you don't ever want it to happen again, but in those ways, it's been, I think, a very enlightening year.

Q: That definitely makes sense. I don't know if you've had personal experience with this, but do you think some sort of monetary compensation for healthcare workers would help individuals who have experienced wage cuts alongside working longer hours? I don't know if you or any of your peers have had that experience.

A: I haven't. I would say yes to that, but I think that...so, especially here, I feel like healthcare workers were compensated in some states. Well, I'm not sure if that's true across the board though.

"YOU'VE HEARD THAT PEOPLE HAVE DIED,
BUT HAVING TO BE THERE AND SEE IT
HAPPEN IS JUST DIFFERENT"

JUNE 2021 (USA)

Q: When and how did you become interested in medicine?

A: Let's see. Honestly, I find more joy working with people than with papers because I started as a nurse assistant. I used to work with older adults in a nursing home, and then I got a job working as a physical therapy technician, but then I was doing more paperwork than anything else. I found that that didn't work for me. I was just not happy. I missed that personal touch with patients. That's when I decided that I would just become a nurse. Because that would bring me joy, and, I'd be able to get more satisfaction from my patients. That's when I made the decision to further and become a nurse.

Q: In a word, if possible, how would you describe your overall experience during the pandemic, both as a nurse and as an individual going through a worldwide pandemic for the first time?

A: Uncertainty. Because it's like you go to work, but you're just hoping and praying that things go well, that nobody dies on your shift. And that you also don't get infected. It was, like, every day comes with uncertainty. "I hope nothing happens." You're uncertain because you can't predict the future. You never know what's going to happen. That's how I would describe it.

Q: What does your unit work on?

A: I worked on a cardiac floor.

Q: How has your experience as a woman in the workplace shaped or influenced the way that you've handled the pandemic, if at all?

A: To me, I feel like being a woman in a workplace...for example, in my unit, we have more women than men. I feel supported a lot because my floor has outstanding teamwork. I think being a woman, especially with how emotional we are sometimes...having that support makes me feel good. That's all I can think of.

Q: What was the most challenging part of the pandemic and what could have been done to make it better?

A: I think the most challenging part for me...I'm a people person. I love to hug. I like that personal touch with people, even my patients. Before the pandemic, when I worked with them, if they were having a hard time, sometimes you didn't have to talk to them; you hugged them and gave them a pat on the back. That proximity...that alone can help them calm down and feel good.

But the pandemic just made things so much harder. Sometimes a smile, just a smile, will change many things. The patients can't see that. There's only so much you can do. You can't hug them. When it first hit, many people were scared to get close to patients that had the virus. I think that was the biggest hurdle for me because I was like, "Well, you don't want to touch anybody and then get COVID." But once we found out what it was about, you at least know the closest thing I could do was give them a pat on the back.

I've had patients that have been discharged. They're like, "I want to give you a hug." I'm like, "Oh, sorry, because of COVID, I can't." But you can hold their hands and give them that pat. That was the biggest thing for me.

Q: *Was there something else that you used instead to comfort patients since you couldn't interact with them as intimately?*

A: What I did, although it was a little crazy...I would draw a smile on my mask and put eyes on it. They'll see it, then they'll smile, and I'm like, "Yeah. It's because I can't give you a smile or a hug. So, this was my way of working with it." And it didn't just affect patients...even my coworkers, doctors. It eased the tension in the unit, which was great. Or sometimes, on the face shield, you draw some small eyes and a smile, which keeps things going. The minor things can make a difference.

Q: Was there any specific experience or moment that was resonated with you that you would be comfortable sharing?

A: Although this isn't related to COVID, it's when I lost my first patient. It was two months ago because I'm a new nurse. This was two months ago. Honestly, I had only been with the patient for two hours, and then he just died. Because he went for dialysis, I didn't see him when I came on the shift. And then he came back. I fed him. I'd forgotten one of his meds, so I was going to grab it. It was a non-essential medication. The doctors came, and then we spoke. Because it's a telemetry floor, if our patient's rhythm changes, they would call you to let you know, "The patient's rhythm or the pulse is super low. Go check in on the patient."

I got the call. And the patient was in an isolation room, so I got the call and put my stuff on. I went in there. Couldn't feel a pulse. But then the thing was that he was a "Do not attempt to resuscitate" patient. Then I was like, "Man, what should I do? What should I do?

I pushed the code blue button to get help. People came in, the doctors came in, and they checked, and that was it. He was gone. It took me a while, too, yeah. I couldn't even be there to help clean him up and all. My manager took me away because I was crying all over the place. After all, I couldn't handle it. You've heard that people have died but having to be there and see it happen is just different. After that, I thought, "I don't want to be on a floor where I get to see people die." It's inevitable. You can't do anything about it but do your best. I was able to talk to the family and sympathize with them because it was just different because it was their first time seeing me. I think it made me appreciate life a lot more.

Q: *I'm assuming your peers are also dealing with loss a lot - especially those who have been there longer. Is there something that they do to handle the losses that they face?*

A: Well, I know they just started a book club, and there is a resource, I believe, in the hospital, where you can go and then talk. When I began during COVID, our unit had moved them. Because they were telling me that when COVID hit and there were like five, six people who coded and died within a day in the unit, they were, like...it was just terrible emotionally. It was just crazy.

Also, the fact that many nurses quit at the time too made it even harder. Many of them said they turn to their family for that emotional support and whatever that makes them feel good. But then the hospital has resources that help us. Like when I lost my patient, my manager spoke to me. She was like...I could go to them to talk, and they would help me. But thankfully, I have a great support system, so I didn't have to do that.

Q: I've seen issues like mental health and sometimes physical disabilities affect female and non-binary healthcare workers disproportionately. Have you or any of your peers had experiences with these issues, if you're comfortable sharing that?

A: Well, not for me. But one of my classmates used to work in the ICU, but he switched to our floor because he said he realized with time that he was getting burned out because he started earlier, before us. And the ICU is mainly COVID. He said he experienced so much death...he couldn't deal with it. He moved to our floor because we don't have COVID patients. Now that it's a stable unit, you don't see code blues. There'll be more of a stat team, and then we send them to the ICU kind of thing.

He said he couldn't deal with it. Even now, I've noticed that when something happens, or a patient is deteriorating, he gets super anxious. We have to try to talk to him. We're like, "It's okay, hang in there. You got this. Take a moment. Take a breather." Or like, "Stand back, and then we'll take care of things." That's what I've seen. It's not easy dealing with something like that.

Q: Do you believe the mainstream media is covering the experiences of healthcare workers accurately? Is there something you think they're missing out on?

A: I think they sometimes forget that we, as nurses, have emotions. We get tired. Listen, you're on your feet for 12, 16, 14 hours. How long? I think the hardest thing is...let's say you have five patients. One you can see as actively dying. You go in there, you talk to them, you sympathize with them. But then you go to the next room, and that person is better, getting ready to go home, and you have to smile. It's like, you have to keep switching emotions like a light switch. That's very draining.

The media doesn't focus on the mental health of nurses. I think it's more of what can bring them views or money or stuff like that. I don't believe even healthcare gets as much attention as it should. Unfortunately, that's the kind of world we live in, so you learn to deal with it.

Q: Do you feel represented in your field?

A: I feel like nurses are very underappreciated. Especially before this pandemic, I would say. It was after the pandemic or during that people started appreciating nurses. Like something happens, maybe a patient hits a nurse, but no matter what, I've seen that Patient Relations always takes the patient's side without listening to the nurse. A friend of mine has experienced something like that. They even found out that the patient's family was the one

who made a mistake, but they never even bothered to apologize to the nurse. Little things like these make you wonder, "Why bother if I'm going to be very underappreciated for doing my best?" Do you know?

Thankfully, the male doctors are pretty chill. And sometimes, I'm glad that they even listen to us because I don't know what I would do if they didn't.

Because I'm like, "Hey, we got to do this and do that and do that." They're like, "Oh yeah. You're thinking ahead of the blocks. Thank you."

Q: *That's awesome.*

A: Yeah, I've had good experiences so far. And our female doctors are rocking it.

Q: *What message do you have for the public as a nurse?*

A: If it were during COVID, I'd say, "Please wear your masks." Now I say I want to encourage people to take good care of themselves because it's like they don't realize how much the things they do in their everyday lives tend to affect them down the road. Because there are so many things that they could avoid early in life. Like even just having regular checkups, things as little as that could help you catch certain things at an earlier stage instead of waiting for it to worsen when nothing can be done.

Unfortunately, I've realized in this area that our Spanish-speaking folks tend to neglect the little things such as going in for doctor's checkups and all that. We find that they're young, and then they come in, and their kidneys are already messed up. That's a considerable concern that I've seen so far since I started working as a nurse. I feel like we have to bring this to their attention.

Q: *Over the course of the pandemic, what could have been done better? Do you see anything positive that has come out of it?*

A: I wasn't there during the pandemic, so I don't have much to tell you. I don't know how they did things; I've only heard.

Q: *In your field in general, what could have been done better with regards to preparing for the pandemic?*

A: Let me see. Maybe, I guess, if we had more information earlier, we would have known how to deal with this better. Then perhaps we wouldn't have lost that many patients like we did. Because I think at the beginning, it's like no one knew what to do. Apparently, from what I've heard, pretty much anyone that codes doesn't make it. I'll end it there.

Q: *Is there another story or experience that my questions haven't covered that you would like to share?*

A: Not much. Just...nursing is fulfilling. It's tiring, it's exhausting. We love it, however.

"YOU HAVE TO DEAL WITH TRYING TO KEEP YOUR FAMILY SAFE, YOUR PATIENTS SAFE , AND YOURSELF SAFE"

JULY 2021 (USA)

Q: How did you become interested in medicine?

A: I guess it all started back in high school. I took an intro to health careers. And it was a course that introduced you to everything from nursing to dentistry, stuff like that. Then I thought I'd go the nursing route, changed my mind, did bio stuff, went to the pharmacy, and came back around to nursing because I liked working with people. I worked in a lab, and I was lonely. I missed making connections with patients, and I felt the urge to help people.

Q: In a word, or if that's not possible, a phrase, how would you describe your overall experience during the pandemic?

A: I'd say stressful.

Q: What has been the most stressful part?

A: Probably just the uncertainty of the outcomes related to COVID, health-wise and the long-term effects it has on people and never knowing the best thing to do for your family, I think, is highly stressful.

Q: How has your experience as a woman in the workplace or a female nurse shaped or influenced, if at all, the way that you or your peers have handled the pandemic?

A: Well, I think I have an interesting perspective as I'm a new mom. Being a mom and a woman during the pandemic, in the healthcare field, is just a little overwhelming at times because you have to deal with trying to keep your family safe, your patients safe, and yourself safe. So, I graduated nursing school during the pandemic, I had my baby during the pandemic, and I started my job during the pandemic. So, it's been rough. It's been a challenge.

Q: *What could have been done to make it better, specifically for you as a new mom?*

A: Yeah, I think having all family members comply with the guidelines, if that were something to be controlled. Honestly, I feel like my workplace did a pretty good job with it. Besides proper PPE, I wish that N95s were more available to all of us. They are not, but...yeah, that would have helped too.

Q: *Was there a shortage of them?*

A: I think, overall, in the country, there's a shortage. They weren't just letting us have them. If there was a suspected case, I think we could get them, but it was me being a new employee. You have to go through this long process to be fitted and everything for the N95, and they were short-staffed. They didn't get into that.

Q: *Are you working in the COVID patient ward, or are you working in a different ward?*

A: No, I am with the oncology patients.

Q: *Just for my knowledge, what impact has the pandemic had on your patients or just the way that your workplace has operated?*

A: I think it's been tough on the patients. The patients who come to my unit are incredibly sick; they've exhausted many other treatment options. And many of them who come in for their treatments have to be alone. They can't have the visitors in the hospitals anymore, and it just puts that extra stressor on them. It's just an emotional time for them to begin with, and without having that support system there with them, it's just been extremely tough.

Q: *Have nurses been expected to provide emotional support for the patients in any way?*

A: Oh, yeah. I mean, that's part of the nurse's role too, but it's different having your family members versus a healthcare worker.

Q: *How do you approach giving that support in a very stressful time?*

A: Sure. Takes a lot of time management in the workplace. You have to get the tasks done, like giving the medicine, whatever, and make sure you get all of those done, but leave that time to sit with the patient, talk with them, hold their hand, and listen. I think therapeutic silence goes a very long way. Just being there, being physically present for them, I think, goes a long way.

Q: Is there any specific experience that you would like to share or a powerful story that resonated with you?

A: Well, I had a patient, I guess, going through what's called CAR T-cell therapy. It makes you sick. Once you start having that immune response, the patients get incredibly ill. They spike fevers. They can be confused, just out of it. So, when they go through it, it's essential to make that time to be with them, to tell them it's going to be okay, they're going to get through this, to make them feel better and advocate for them as well, because sometimes, the physicians don't want to treat the symptoms so much. So, you got to be there and advocate for them to give that Tylenol to bring the fever down. It's been a lot like that. Just really advocating for them when they don't have anybody to do it for them.

Q: Is there a particular reason they don't want to treat the symptoms?

A: Well, it's not so much that they don't want to treat them. It's research. So, anything you add to the patient, they have to account for the study, which becomes a variable.

Well, for example, I talked about the fevers -

sometimes they don't want to give Tylenol because they wish for that immune response, they want to see it because that's one of the ways they can tell it's working, but sometimes these patients just become so...so miserable with it that they need it.

Q: *How do you move on in such an emotionally taxing job?*

A: COVID, on top of everything in the oncology realm...it can be pretty emotionally taxing because these people are at the end of the line sometimes. And it's just coming home to my family, giving them big hugs, and unwinding by talking through it... sometimes with coworkers, sometimes with my family, just really having someone to listen to, to vent to a little bit. I think it's rewarding, though, because you get to be that support system for the patients. And I think, yes, it's sad, but also, you get to provide strength, which I think helps get through it too.

Q: *Do you communicate with the patients' families at all?*

A: Now that things are opening back up a little bit, yes. During COVID, no. No one was allowed in here, and we don't usually give out information over the phone because of HIPAA. So, we didn't communicate with families.

Q: I've read some studies that mental health issues and musculoskeletal diseases affect women, specifically female healthcare workers, in worse ways than they affect men. Do you have any personal experience with these issues, or have you primarily seen some of them in your peers? Have you heard a lot of stories of burnout during the pandemic?

A: Oh, yeah. Oh, yeah. There's a burnout. And I think, now that we're starting to come out of things, people are beginning to realize that they're burnt out. I see it in my coworkers a lot; they're just dreading coming to work. We don't work in a COVID unit, but with all the outside stressors...and, like you said, everybody's experiencing loss differently. Everybody's just becoming burnt out in their unit.

Q: Was your unit restricted in any way because of COVID? Could you not let in as many patients?

A: Oh, yeah. We have double capacity rooms, but they've all been single patient rooms the entire time. Yeah. Yeah. So, that's cut down. Yeah. And they were enrolling less, to begin with, because a lot of our patients are surgical. So, they weren't doing as many surgeries if they weren't life-threatening. It cut down on the patient population.

Q: Do you feel that the mainstream media is covering the pandemic regarding female and non-binary frontline workers accurately? Is there something that you think they're missing out on?

A: Well, I think, in the beginning, they were. I think it's died out. Because in the beginning, I feel like they did try to cover. They mentioned burnout. They said there's a lack of PPE. I feel like social media was an excellent place to go for that. People venting on social media more than, I guess, the news outlets and stuff.

Q: *Do you think those were useful? Were those expressions of support on social media helpful to you and your peers?*

A: I don't think it was enough. It was helpful to see that people recognized the struggle.

Q: *Was there something that could have helped? What could people have done in the media to support healthcare workers during this time in a more concrete way or a better way?*

A: I think it was just tough on everybody. I don't know if there was anything that honestly could have been done better, besides having the proper equipment and everything to deal with, like appropriate staffing.

Q: *Do you feel represented in your field? Do you feel represented in medicine, in general?*

A: *I* think I do. Yeah. I mean, honestly, nursing

is a pretty female-heavy profession, and at least in my workplace, they try to involve nurses in the care of the patients. And in the way the facility functions, we have a thing called shared governance. So, you can be involved in committees. I think my facility is supportive of nurses and women. Yeah. There are many women in leadership roles.

Q: I know you touched on this, but is there anything that has been explicitly keeping you going and motivated? What has been keeping your peers motivated?

A: I think trying to help people. That's it, honestly. When most people get into nursing and healthcare, they want to make people feel better. They want to support them in knowing that you can...or even if you do a little thing for a patient during the day, like, I don't know, give them a cookie or something. It just helps make their day better, and you feel good about doing it. I think that's what keeps a lot of people going.

Q: Do you think some mental health initiative to help with the burnout would have helped healthcare workers? I've heard about how many healthcare workers are quitting, unfortunately. Would some mental health initiative help with that?

A: I think so. I know some...they call it

debriefing on specific units where something traumatic happens, and you get together. So sometimes, bring in a psychiatrist or a social worker or something to talk through it. And I think that needs to be done everywhere more often.

Q: *Is that only done in specific units? Is it done in your team?*

A: No. But I think it should be.

Q: *Is there a specific unit that it's done in? Is there a reason why it exists in some departments? and not in others?*

A: I think the ICU does it. Yeah. Right. But I mean, traumatic things happen in every unit. My unit gets codes. My team receives some stressful stuff. But I think overall, it would help, no matter what the unit is.

Q: *Do you see anything positive that has come out of the pandemic?*

A: That's a unique question. Well, I think it showed how resilient people could be. Showed how resilient healthcare workers can be. I know there is talk of many people quitting, but many people stay in it and want to power through and help where they can. And I think it's pretty impressive.

Q: *Is there a part of your experience that my questions haven't been touched on yet that you would like to share?*

A: I don't know. I think you hit a lot of them.

Q: What message do you have for the public?

A: Be kind to healthcare workers. We want to help.

Q: Do you think some economic compensation would help, or is the bigger issue the emotional trauma that healthcare workers are facing?

A: Honestly, probably both. Presumably a mix.

Q: Were there wage cuts for healthcare workers where you work?

A: No. So, we were blessed.

Q: Is there a unique story or experience, maybe with a patient or something else that resonated with you that my previous questions haven't addressed yet?

A: No, I don't think so.

SURVEYS

"DEALING WITH AN INVISIBLE ENEMY"

JANUARY 2021 (France)

Q: How did you become interested/involved in your profession?

A: I always knew I would be a doctor since the age of 8. It was just evident, and I still can't explain it.

Q: In one word or phrase, how would you describe your overall experience during the pandemic?

A: It seems like the beginning of a new world, a new period, dealing with an invisible enemy.

Q: What was the hardest part of the pandemic?

A: Dealing with the distress and anxiety of patients.

Q: How has the pandemic evolved between March and now?

A: We learn to live with it. We have had a better period with fewer ill patients, but it is now increasing again very fast.

Q: Do you see anything positive that has come out of the pandemic?

A: People are washing their hands and now having the mask when they are ill and coughing!! So, less flu!

Q: How has your experience as a woman in the workplace shaped or influenced how you handle the pandemic?

A: As a woman, I am more attentive to the

whole patient and his feelings. I am also listening and trying to help them deal with the stress, not only treating the body.

Q: *Do you feel represented in your profession?*

A: More and more!

Q: *Is there any specific experience that you would like to share? A significant story?*

A: A lot of patients with hyperventilation syndrome...it's due to anxiety. This pandemic causes a lot of collateral damages. I keep on telling my patients to stop watching T.V. all day long.

Q: *What is it that keeps you going and motivated? What keeps your peers motivated?*

A: The need to serve people.

Q: *How have you handled the concept of loss during the pandemic?*

A: This wasn't a new concept for me, dealing with lung cancer every day.

Q: *Do you feel like mainstream media coverage is covering the pandemic regarding female frontline workers accurately? Is there something that you think that they are missing out on?*

A: No, I don't think so.

Q: *Is there a unique story or experience that my previous questions have not addressed yet that you would like to share?*

A: No. Good luck!

"FEELING FEARFUL OF LITTLE THINGS"

JANUARY 2021(Brazil)

Q: How did you become interested/involved in your profession?

A: By the end of high school, I was in doubt about which career to choose. My father suggested to me, "Why don't you try medicine?" I have always been a good student at school, so I had the opportunity to choose between different courses at university. I decided to listen to my father's advice. By the beginning of my medicine course, I still had many doubts. But little by little, I had started to see myself as a doctor, especially in my fourth year, when I studied Pediatrics.

Q: In one word or phrase, how would you describe your overall experience during the pandemic?

A: CARE.

Q: What was the hardest part of the pandemic?

A: I think it is feeling fearful of little things. I mean, little things that used to be simple in our day by day, such as a hug, having a snack during my job, touching a public computer...now all of those little things are different because they can represent a risk to our health. Even drinking water at work needs a "protocol" (sanitize hands, take the mask and glasses off, sanitize hands, drink water, put the mask, and glasses on, sanitize hands again).

Another disturbing thing here, in Brazil, is that we can't trust our government. Our Health Ministry sometimes spreads fake news and misinformation, such as a hydroxychloroquine treatment for everybody.

Sometimes I have double work because I explain everything, I know to a COVID patient. The next day, the same patient sends me messages because he found different information on the Health Ministry page. I have to explain everything again.

Q: *How has the pandemic evolved between March and now?*

A: I think, at the beginning, people were more afraid of SARS-Cov2. Now, we are in a "second wave" of the pandemic, but people in Brazil keep going to restaurants and gymnastic clubs! There are even some people that say that wearing a mask isn't necessary anymore! We are now having a terrible time in the north of Brazil, but some Brazilians keep going, like we are not in the pandemic anymore.

Q: *Do you see anything positive that has come out of the pandemic?*

A: Yes! I could spend more time with my daughters! One of my jobs allows me to work online. I can stay near them! I think this pandemic made me see the fundamental importance of my family.

I have a seven-month-old baby, and it was good to have the opportunity to be a little bit closer to her.

Q: *How has your experience as a woman in the workplace shaped or influenced how you handle the pandemic?*

A: I think the pandemic shaped the way I do things in my house. And as a woman, I feel more overloaded at home. But I don't know if my experience as a woman influenced how I handled the pandemic. Maybe I try to be more careful because I feel afraid to bring SARS-CoV2 to my house. I think about my daughters and my mom, and I have to be extra cautious not to bring SARS-CoV2 to my house.

Q: *Do you feel represented in your profession?*

A: In Brazil, part of the debate and information about COVID-19 is mixed with politics. Some doctors support our president and, if the president says hydroxychloroquine is a good treatment, these doctors prescribe hydroxychloroquine. And as doctors, I believe we should keep our decisions based on science. Sometimes, as a doctor, I feel ashamed of some attitudes of other doctors. Fortunately, the majority of doctors that work with me and those that are my friends are trying to keep loyal to science and not to politics.

Q: What is it that keeps you going and motivated? What keeps your peers motivated?

A: I don't know. It is one day at a time. My biggest desire is to get well at the end of the pandemic and not lose any one of my family or close friends.

Q: How have you handled the concept of loss during the pandemic?

A: Fortunately, I am not working in hospitals. Nowadays, I work in a genetic lab, and I make pediatric appointments online, so I do not have to handle the concept of loss so often in my job.

Of course, the pandemic impacts us. We see so many deaths on the news. We get sad and afraid. Personally, sometimes I prefer not to watch TV or read the information so that I can protect my mind better, preserving my mental health.

Q: Do you feel like mainstream media coverage is covering the pandemic regarding female frontline workers accurately? Is there something that you think that they are missing out on?

A: I think it is now, at the pandemic, the same as it was before the pandemic. Mainstream media generally shows more the work of male doctors and male health authorities than female doctors and female health authorities. It didn't change during the pandemic.

"EVERY ASPECT OF MY LIFE WAS IMPACTED"

MARCH 2021 (USA)

Q: How did you become interested/involved in your profession?

A: Family tradition.

Q: In one word or phrase, how would you describe your overall experience during the pandemic?

A: Uncertainty.

Q: What was the hardest part of the pandemic?

A: I lost my job.

Q: How has the pandemic evolved between March and now?

A: Every aspect of my life was impacted.

Q: Do you see anything positive that has come out of the pandemic?

A: Mother nature is taking a break. Very positive!

Q: How has your experience as a woman in the workplace shaped or influenced how you handle the pandemic?

A: In general, women are more careful. As a healthcare worker, I had the information and the tools since the pandemic started.

Q: Do you feel represented in your profession?

A: No, I don't.

Q: Is there any specific experience that you would like to share? A significant story?

A: Sadly, as a woman, I do not make the same money as men for the same tasks.

Q: What is it that keeps you going and motivated? What keeps your peers motivated?

A: Everything is changing. Women are more vital than ever.

Q: How have you handled the concept of loss during the pandemic?

A: I always think about others who are in a worse situation than me.

Q: Do you feel like mainstream media coverage is covering the pandemic regarding female frontline workers accurately? Is there something that you think that they are missing out on?

A: In my opinion, the media listened to leaders more than science.

Q: Is there a unique story or experience that my previous questions have not addressed yet that you would like to share?

A: No.

" IF YOU ARE A HEALTHCARE WORKER

WORKING IN THE HOSPITAL DURING THIS

PANDEMIC, IT IS

MORE FULFILLING"

MARCH 2021 (USA)

Q: How did you become interested/involved in your profession?

A: Healthcare is my passion; I love working with sick people.

Q: In one word or phrase, how would you describe your overall experience during the pandemic?

A: More challenging. If you are a healthcare worker working in the hospital during this pandemic, it is more fulfilling.

Q: What was the hardest part of the pandemic?

A: Going to work in the hospital and coming home to my family.

Q: How has the pandemic evolved between March and now?

A: It has been very terrible for the past four months, but now the virus is decreasing.

Q: Do you see anything positive that has come out of the pandemic?

A: Yes, since the vaccine is available, a lot of people are getting it. This virus will end soon.

Q: Do you feel represented in your profession?

A: Yes since I tried to educate any family member.

Q: What is it that keeps you going and motivated? What keeps your peers motivated?

A: Moments that individuals you are with are inspiring at times...that each and every person has a support system.

"NURSES HAVE BEEN ASKED TO MAKE

SACRIFICES WITH NOTHING IN RETURN"

FEBRUARY 2021 (USA)

Q: How did you become interested/involved in your profession?

A: My family had a terrible car accident. My son was critically injured, and I became a nurse to understand his needs better and care for him.

Q: In one word or phrase, how would you describe your overall experience during the pandemic?

A: Stressful.

Q: What was the hardest part of the pandemic?

A: Going to work, not knowing who may have COVID and I might bring it home to my family.

Q: How has the pandemic evolved between March and now?

A: Even though there are still more new cases than in March 2020, people seem to be less careful.

Q: Do you see anything positive that has come out of the pandemic?

A: Hopefully better respiratory etiquette. Maybe people will wear masks when they are sick now.

Q: How has your experience as a woman in the workplace shaped or influenced how you handle the pandemic?

A: It has been harder to handle housework and errands and working. There is no time to do anything with homeschooling and kids home all day.

Q: Do you feel represented in your profession?

A: No, it feels like nurses have been asked to make many sacrifices with little in return.

Q: Is there any specific experience that you would like to share? A significant story?

A: A patient kept getting mad that we were not ruling him out for COVID. He was angry at all the PPE you had to wear, and he kept saying we were afraid of COVID.

Q: What is it that keeps you going and motivated? What keeps your peers motivated?

A: I feel needed. I want to take care of people.

Q: How have you handled the concept of loss during the pandemic?

A: We have lost so much this year. I am trying to think of it as a long pause and hopefully get back to normal soon.

Q: Do you feel like mainstream media coverage is covering the pandemic regarding female frontline workers accurately? Is there something that you think they are missing out on?

A: Just how much women are being asked to do now.

Q: Is there a unique story or experience that my previous questions have not addressed yet that you would like to share?

A: No.

"FOOD SERVICE AND HOUSEKEEPING

CHALLENGES IS MISSING IN MEDIA

COVERAGE"

MARCH 2021 (USA)

Q: *How did you become interested/involved in your profession?*

A: There is security in the healthcare field.

Q: *In one word or phrase, how would you describe your overall experience during the pandemic?*

A: Scary.

Q: *What was the hardest part of the pandemic?*

A: Constant policy changes (masks).

Q: *How has the pandemic evolved between March and now?*

A: More minor precautions now.

Q: *Do you see anything positive that has come out of the pandemic?*

A: Less census in the hospital.

Q: *Do you feel represented in your profession?*

A: Yes.

Q: *Is there any specific experience that you would like to share? A significant story?*

A: No.

Q: *What is it that keeps you going and motivated? What keeps your peers motivated?*

A: Family.

Q: *How have you handled the concept of loss during the pandemic?*

A: I have not dealt with it personally.

Q: Do you feel like mainstream media coverage is covering the pandemic regarding female frontline workers accurately? Is there something that you think that they are missing out on?

A: Food service and housekeeping coverage are missing.

WE HAVE TO FIGHT AGAINST ALL ODDS

MARCH 2021(USA)

Q: How did you become interested/involved in your profession?

A: As an essential worker, I got involved in my profession.

Q: In one word or phrase, how would you describe your overall experience during the pandemic?

A: It's scary.

Q: What was the hardest part of the pandemic?

A: Kids got stuck at home and were not able to get out.

Q: How has the pandemic evolved between March and now?

A: It's pretty familiar now.

Q: Do you see anything positive that has come out of the pandemic?

A: Yes, the environment will get some time to heal.

Q: How has your experience as a woman in the workplace shaped or influenced how you handle the pandemic?

A: Kids stay at home and attend home school. That makes a huge difference in life, and they need to adjust to every aspect of life.

Q: Do you feel represented in your profession?

A: It makes me feel better to represent myself in

my work.

Q: *What is it that keeps you going and motivated? What keeps your peers motivated?*

A: We have to fight against all odds.

" PEOPLE SUPPORT AND HELP EACH OTHER"

FEBRUARY 2021 (USA)

Q: How did you become interested/involved in your profession?

A: My mom influenced me to become a nurse.

Q: In one word or phrase, how would you describe your overall experience during the pandemic?

A: Challenging.

Q: What was the hardest part of the pandemic?

A: Limited gathering with family and friends, getting sick, seeing your loved ones dying due to COVID, and seeing patients suffering from COVID.

Q: How has the pandemic evolved between March and now?

A: The good side is people become more aware of how to clean and protect themselves, and the bad side is people have become paranoid.

Q: Do you see anything positive that has come out of the pandemic?

A: People support and help each other.

Q: Is there any specific experience that you would like to share? A significant story?

A: We got hit with this pandemic/COVID, but sometimes we do not get enough support battling it, well, most of the time.

Q: What is it that keeps you going and motivated? What keeps your peers motivated?

A: There are always ups and downs, but we still need to move on and keep living.

Q: How have you handled the concept of loss during the pandemic?

A: Pray for your loved ones and grieve for the ones we lost.

Q: Do you feel like mainstream media coverage is covering the pandemic regarding female frontline workers accurately? Is there something that you think that they are missing out on?

A: I don't think so. They are missing a lot of support; the media focuses on things that they should not be focused on.

Q: Is there a unique story or experience that my previous questions have not addressed yet that you would like to share?

A: The government needs to focus on supporting frontliners and healthcare workers.

"GRATITUDE KEEPS ME GOING"

April 2021 (USA)

Q: How did you become interested/involved in your profession?

A: I was always interested in nutrition and health growing up. I decided to go to college and study nutrition.

Q: In one word or phrase, how would you describe your overall experience during the pandemic?

A: Uncertain.

Q: What was the hardest part of the pandemic?

A: Dealing with the fear and unknowns of a new virus.

Q: How has the pandemic evolved between March and now?

A: We are now more knowledgeable about the virus.

Q: Do you see anything positive that has come out of the pandemic?

A: People get to spend more time with their family.

Q: How has your experience as a woman in the workplace shaped or influenced the way you handle the pandemic?

A: It has not.

Q: Do you feel represented in your profession?

A: No.

Q: Is there any specific experience that you would like to share? A significant story?

A: No.

Q: What is it that keeps you going and motivated? What keeps your peers motivated?

A: Gratitude keeps me going.

Q: Do you feel like mainstream media coverage is covering the pandemic regarding female frontline workers accurately? Is there something that you think that they are missing out on?

A: Not sure.

Q: Is there a unique story or experience that my previous questions have not addressed yet that you would like to share?

A: No.

Acknowledgments

This book would not exist without the support of the health-care workers I interviewed - whether their experiences were published or not, I was struck by their resilience and determination. I would also like to acknowledge the healthcare workers who reviewed this book and provided me with the vital information that would help me understand the vast and complex array of issues that surrounds the experience of being a female or non-binary healthcare worker during the COVID-19 pandemic. A special thanks to Dr. Bindu Chopra for her support throughout the process.

Made in the USA
Columbia, SC
20 October 2021